The Biology of Higher Cryptogams

Cover photo of *Asterella bolanderi*.

CURRENT CONCEPTS IN BIOLOGY
A Macmillan Series
NORMAN H. GILES, WALTER KENWORTHY, JOHN G. TORREY, Editors

The Biology of
Higher Cryptogams

William T. Doyle

University of California, Santa Cruz

The Macmillan Company
Collier-Macmillan Limited, London

First Printing

Library of Congress catalog card number: 73–84436

The Macmillan Company

Collier-Macmillan Canada, Ltd., Toronto, Ontario

Printed in the United States of America

Preface

THIS BOOK is about the land plants that do not form seeds, about their life and development. I have tried to present the material at a level comprehensible to a student with only an elementary background in biology, especially in cell structure and function.

One of my reasons for writing this book is that it provided me with the opportunity to discuss the land plants, particularly the higher cryptogams, as a natural evolutionary group. All too often the bryophytes are treated as nonvascular plants along with the algae and fungi, whereas the other land plants are discussed separately as vascular plants. I feel that this treatment tends to obscure the basic relationship between bryophytes and the other land plants. Chapters 2 and 3 deal with the uniformity in the basic plan of higher cryptogams. They have a similar type of life cycle and they appear to have evolved from similar ancestors, if not from a common ancestor. An introduction to some of the diversity that has developed during the long evolutionary history of each group of higher cryptogams is presented in Chapter 4. Chapter 5 discusses a few of the developmental stages in the higher cryptogams and the use of these plants in developmental biological research. Most of the references cited in the text are found in the Selected Bibliography at the end of the book. Most of the citations are to the original research papers in order to introduce students to original research literature.

I am particularly grateful to Miss Shirley Gould, Mrs. Carole Kelley, Miss Myrna Steinkamp, Mr. M. Gene Wolery, and my wife, Glendawyn Doyle, for reading and criticizing the original manuscript and for many helpful suggestions. I also wish to thank the many contributors who have generously allowed me to use their photographs and illustrations in this book. Their contributions are credited in the captions accompanying the figures.

W. T. D.

Contents

The Biology of Higher Cryptogams

Introduction to the Higher Cryptogams

THE TERM *cryptogam* most likely has very little meaning to the average elementary biology student, and *higher cryptogam* is even more obscure. The function of this first chapter is to define the terms and briefly to describe current views on the relationship of the higher cryptogams to other plants and to each other.

What Are Cryptogams?

Cryptogam comes from the Greek words *kruptos* meaning "hidden," and *gamos* meaning "wedded." This allusion to hidden sexuality is of historical interest in that plants now recognized as fungi, algae, and bryophytes were at one time classified in the single class Cryptogamia. The seed plants were placed in the contrasting class Phanerogamia, meaning "open-wedded." The "hidden" sexuality of the Cryptogamia resulted from lack of knowledge. Sexuality has since been described for the majority of cryptogams, and the term has fallen into general disuse in recent years. Nonetheless, it remains a useful term to encompass, in a single word, plants that reproduce by spores rather than seeds. The algae and fungi are treated in a separate book in this series; the biology of the remaining spore-producing plants, the so-called higher cryptogams, is the subject of this book. These plants are the bryophytes (hornworts, liverworts, and mosses), psilopsids, lycopsids, sphenopsids, and ferns.

Relationships

There is little doubt that higher cryptogams and the seed plants, together called land plants or embryophytes, either evolved from green algal ancestors or had common ancestry with green algae. This conclusion is based on the following kinds of evidence: The chloroplasts of both green algae and land plants contain chlorophylls *a* and *b* (Figure 1·1A), and many of the carotenoid pigments are similar. The carbohydrate food reserve, called green plant or "true" starch to differentiate it from starches found in other plant groups, is identical. In both green algae and land plants the starch grain contains a mixture of two kinds of glucose macromolecules, amylose and amylopectin (Figure 1·1B,D,F). Amylose is an unbranched, long-chain α-1,4-linked glucose polymer, and amylopectin is a branched glucose polymer with a backbone of α-1,4 glycosidic linkages and with α-1,6 glycosidic linkages at branch points. Additional similarity in carbohydrate metabolism is noted when cell wall structure and composition are compared. For example, the cells of land plants and of many green algae characteristically are surrounded by a pectic wall layer that contains galacturonic acid (Figure 1·1C) and a wall layer containing cellulose. Cellulose, an unbranched, long-chain glucose polymer, resembles the amylose fraction of starch but has β-1,4 linkages (Figure 1·1E). The rigidity of the cell is due, in large part, to the presence of cellulose. Another item of similarity between land plants and green algae is the form of the flagellum. Flagellated cells in land plants are restricted to male gametes, and in all cases the flagella, like those of green algae, are of the whiplash type. Whiplash flagella are elongate and exhibit great flexibility during flagellar beat. They are naked structures; lateral appendages (variously called mastigonemes, flimmer, or tinsel) do not occur. Only green algae and green land plants have this particular combination of characteristics: chlorophylls *a* and *b,* "true" starch, whiplash flagella, and similar cell structure. Thus at the level of cell structure and metabolic pathways, green algae and embryophytes have much in common. Differences exist primarily at the tissue level of differentiation.

Different combinations of characteristics are used to identify the other major plant groups (Table 1·1). The scheme of classification favored by this author is presented in Table 1·2. This scheme, an attempt to indicate the major evolutionary lines, graphically illustrates the current belief that land plants have genic continuity with green algae. However, many botanists have their own ideas about how plants should be classified to reflect phylogenetic relationships and may prefer to use another classification scheme. The organization of this book is such that it can be used with a number of different systems.

As indicated earlier, this author believes that the higher cryptogams belong to the green plant line of evolution, the Chlorophyta, where with the seed plants they comprise one of the major subdivisions, that

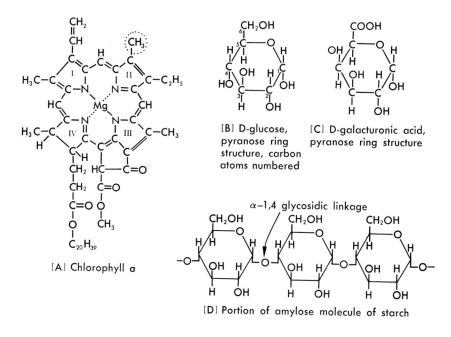

[A] Chlorophyll a

[B] D-glucose, pyranose ring structure, carbon atoms numbered

[C] D-galacturonic acid, pyranose ring structure

α–1,4 glycosidic linkage

[D] Portion of amylose molecule of starch

β–1,4 glycosidic linkage

[E] Portion of cellulose molecule

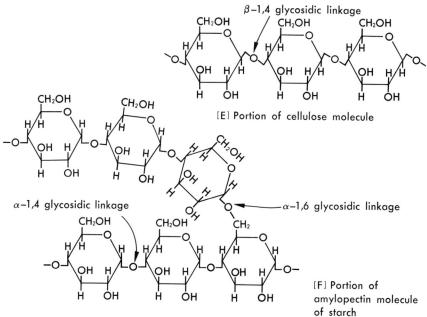

α–1,4 glycosidic linkage

α–1,6 glycosidic linkage

[F] Portion of amylopectin molecule of starch

Figure 1·1. A: Molecule of chlorophyll a. Individual pyrrole nuclei are numbered I–IV. For chlorophyll b, replace —CH₃ with —CHO. **B–F: Carbohydrates and glycosidic linkages characteristic of green plants.**

3

TABLE 1-1
Comparison of Chlorophyll Pigments, Food Reserves, and Flagellation in the Major Groups of Plants

PLANT GROUP	CHLOROPHYLLS				FOOD RESERVES						FLAGELLA	
	a	b	c	d	"true" starch	paramylon	laminarin	chrysolaminarin	cyanophycean starch	floridean starch	whiplash	tinsel
Green land plants	+	+			+						+	
Green algae	+	+			+						+	+
Euglenoids	+	+				+						+
Xanthophytes	+		+					+			+	+
Brown algae	+		+				+				+	+
Chrysophytes and diatoms	+		+					+			+	+
Dinoflagellates	+		+		+						+	
Blue-green algae	+								+		−	−
Red algae	+			±						+	−	−

4

TABLE 1·2
Plant Classification

TAXONOMIC CATEGORY	COMMON NAME
Division Schizophyta	bacteria
Division Eumycota	true fungi
Division Myxomycota	slime molds
Division Cyanophyta	blue-green algae
Division Rhodophyta	red algae
Division Chrysophyta	golden algae and diatoms
Division Phaeophyta	brown algae
Division Pyrrophyta	dinoflagellates
Division Xanthophyta	yellow-green algae
Division Euglenophyta	euglenoids
Division Chlorophyta	green plants
Subdivision Chlorophycophytina	green algae
Subdivision Embryophytina	embryophytes
Class Bryopsida	bryophytes
Subclass Anthocerotidae	hornworts
Subclass Hepaticidae	liverworts
Subclass Bryidae	mosses
Class Psilopsida	psilopsids
Class Lycopsida	lycopsids
Class Sphenopsida	sphenopsids and horsetails
Class Pteropsida	ferns
Class Spermopsida	seed plants
Subclass Gymnospermidae	gymnosperms
Subclass Angiospermidae	flowering plants
Series Dicotyledonae	dicots
Series Monocotyledonae	monocots

of the embryophytes. An embryo is here defined as a multicellular young organism, developed from the zygote, that is surrounded by female reproductive tissue. This definition semantically separates the embryophytes from the green algae, which lack embryos as just defined. The successful adaptation of plants to life on land, accompanied by concomitant modification of form and function of plant parts, represents one of the most important steps in the evolution of the plant kingdom. Although most botanists are confident of the genetic relationship between green algae (more specifically, the Ulotrichalean green algae; see Alexopoulos and Bold, 1967, and Doyle, 1964, in Selected Bibliography) and embryophytes, there is less agreement on the details of origin of land plants. Stages intermediate between green

TABLE 1·3
Geologic Timetable and Events in Plant Evolution [1]

ERA	PERIOD	EPOCH	IMPORTANT PLANT EVENTS	BEGINNING IN MILLIONS OF YEARS
CENOZOIC	QUATERNARY	Pleistocene[2]	Rise of genetic programs to improve cultivated plants (man-directed plant evolution).	1
		Pliocene	Speciation of herbaceous plants.	13
		Miocene	Spread of herbaceous dicots.	25
	TERTIARY	Oligocene	Rise of herbaceous angiosperms.	36
		Eocene	World-wide dispersal of woody angiosperms.	58
		Paleocene	Many now extinct genera of woody angiosperms. Modernization of angiosperm families.	63
MESOZOIC	CRETACEOUS		Earliest known pines. Abundant in late Cretaceous.	135
	JURASSIC		Origin of angiosperms? Definite evidence of diatoms.	180
	TRIASSIC		Spread of conifers. Rise of cycads.	230

Era	Period	Event	Millions of years
PALEOZOIC	PERMIAN	Rise of conifers. Extinction of coal swamp flora.	280
	PENNSYLVANIAN ⎫ Carboniferous	Widespread coal swamps; formation of coal beds.	310
	MISSISSIPPIAN ⎭		
	DEVONIAN	Development of coal swamp forests with gymnosperms, lycopsids, sphenopsids and ferns.	345
		By late Devonian a flourishing land flora with psilopsids, lycopsids, sphenopsids, ferns, seed plants?, and bryophytes?	405
		Evidence of brown algae and dinoflagellates.	
	SILURIAN	Cooksonia, the oldest known vascular plant.[3]	425
		Record of probable nonvascular land plants?[4]	
	ORDOVICIAN	Several marine red and green algae.	500
	CAMBRIAN	Evidence of lime-secreting algae.	600
PRECAMBRIAN	LATE PRECAMBRIAN	Definite evidence of eukaryotic organisms.	1,200
	MIDDLE PRECAMBRIAN	Stromatolites of (blue-green) algal origin.	
		Definite records of blue-green algae and bacteria.	2,500?
		Origin of eukaryotic cell?	
	EARLY PRECAMBRIAN	Bacterialike cells and unicellular algalike organisms of age 3,000 million years.	
		Graphites of possible organic origin.	4,500–5,000?
		Origin of prokaryotic cell?	
		Origin of earth.	

[1] Modified from a table provided by Professor Elso S. Barghoorn, Harvard University.

[2] There is evidence that we are in an interglacial period of the Pleistocene, that this epoch continues.

[3] Based upon the marine invertebrate fauna, the Australian strata containing psilopsids and lycopsids, heretofore considered to be of Upper Silurian age, have been reassigned to the Devonian.

[4] See J. M. Schopf, E. Mencher, A. J. Boucot, and H. N. Andrews. "Erect Plants in the Early Silurian of Maine." U.S. Geological Survey, Professional Paper 550–D, 1966, D69–75.

algae and primitive land plants have not been recognized. Moreover, the degree of relationship among land plant groups is still largely a matter of conjecture. The question of whether land plants arose once (monophyletic origin) or more than once (polyphyletic origin) during plant evolution still elicits lively discussion.

The fossil record has yielded invaluable information concerning evolution within major groups of land plants. However, it has not yet been of significant help in unraveling the early history of land plant evolution—the nature of the plants transitional from the water to land or the origin of the major land plant groups. Table 1·3 presents a geologic timetable showing the major geologic periods correlated with significant events in plant evolution. From this table it is seen that fossil remains indicate that plants representing all the classes of green plants had evolved by the mid-Paleozoic and that they appear to have evolved in a relatively short time span. Vegetative remains of probable land plants occur in the early Silurian, and a flourishing, diverse land flora was in existence by the end of the Devonian.

It can be seen from Table 1·2 that the higher cryptogams include five of the six subgroups (classes) of embryophytes. (The class Spermopsida, the seed plants, is outside the scope of this book.) Each higher cryptogam class represents an evolutionary line in existence at least since the Devonian Period. A comparative study of these organisms, in addition to being of interest in itself, will yield information about problems faced by plants during adaptation to land and about how plants overcome these problems. Moreover, as we shall see in later chapters, higher cryptogamous plants present exciting opportunities for the study of processes basic to growth and development. This opportunity results from the higher cryptogam type of life history, to be described in the next chapter.

The Life Cycle

CONCEPTUALLY, the life cycle of the organism is the organism. All too often this is not made clear, and the term *organism* is used in a restricted sense to identify just one developmental phase. For example, when considering a fern, one generally thinks of a plant with characteristic foliage and growth habit. However, this leafy plant represents but one phase in the life cycle of the fern. The life cycle represents the sum of the stages in the development of the individual organism.

The organism, as considered here, is the biological unit of evolution and, therefore, the unit of comparison between different organisms. It should be evident that selection occurs at all stages in development, there being continuous interaction between environment, gene action, and physiological tolerances of the individual. Each step in development is as important to the survival of the organism as any other step. One important consequence of sequential gene action during growth and development is that through mutation and selection any part of the life cycle can be changed; a whole structure or sequence of development can be altered. Stages in a life cycle can be speeded up, slowed down, or completely lost. Recognition of this has particular significance in understanding the biology of higher cryptogams because there are two multicellular growth phases present, one haploid and one diploid. Evolution has generally occurred along different lines and at different rates within each growth phase. Some plant structures (such as stems) have undergone extensive evolutionary modification, whereas others (gametangia, for example) seem to have been more conservative. The resultant diversity offers a wide variety of research opportunities to the biologist. This chapter focuses primarily on the basic nature of the

9

higher cryptogam life cycle and its morphogenetic potentialities. This will be followed by a chapter on some of the significant changes that have occurred in plant form and structure during land adaptation. An introduction to higher cryptogam diversity will be deferred until Chapter 4.

What is generally taught as the "typical" life cycle of a higher cryptogam consists of a regular alternation of a haploid, gamete-producing (gametophyte) generation with a diploid, spore-producing (sporophyte) generation (Figure 2·1). The two generations are distinctly

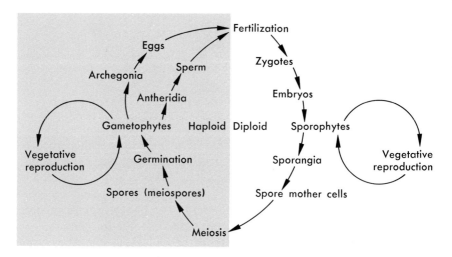

Figure 2·1. Potential "typical" life cycle of higher cryptogams.

dissimilar in form (heteromorphic). In this "typical" cycle the sporophyte develops following fusion of gametes, produced by a multicellular gametophyte, and the gametophyte results from germination of a spore, produced by a multicellular sporophyte. The number of chromosomes is doubled at the time of fertilization and halved prior to spore formation. Although we speak of the regular alternation of these generations, alternation is obligatory only in that a zygote normally gives rise to a sporophyte and a spore gives rise to a gametophyte. However, vegetative reproduction by both generations makes possible the increase in numbers of individuals in either generation without the obligate completion of the life cycle (Figure 2·1).

The Gametophyte and Fertilization

The adult gametophyte may be either short-lived or perennial and it generally remains small in stature. Ordinarily it is photosynthetic, although achlorophyllose and therefore nonphotosynthetic forms are not uncommon. The achlorophyllose gametophytes usually have a subterranean existence and are intimately associated with endophytic fungal hyphae, or they remain quite small, with a limited amount of vegetative growth. Gamete production is the *raison d'être* of the gametophytic generation. Higher cryptogams are oogamous, forming nonflagellated eggs and bi- or multiflagellated sperm. As indicated in Chapter 1, the flagella are of the whiplash type, like those of green algae. The male and female gametes develop within multicellular gametangia, called *antheridia* and *archegonia,* respectively. Antheridia and archegonia have a basically similar structure and development in the higher cryptogams. (It is not necessary at this time to discuss the differences.) Both sex organs may develop on the same individual, the plant in this case being *monoecious,* or the plant may be *dioecious,* with male and female gametangia on separate individuals. (Sex determination and sex expression will be discussed in Chapter 5.)

The mature archegonium is borne on the surface of, or is partially or completely embedded in, gametophytic tissue. The archegonium originates from a single cell which, through a regular sequence of mitotic divisions, gives rise to a multicellular structure consisting of an outer layer surrounding an axial cell row (Figure 2·2A). The cell at the base of the row usually develops into the egg. The cell of the axial row adjacent to the egg is called the *ventral canal cell*. The egg and ventral canal cell lie in the part of the archegonium called the *venter*.

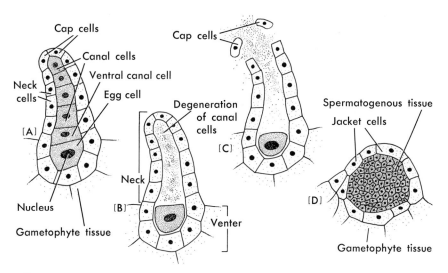

Figure 2·2. Female and male gametangia of higher cryptogams. A: Nearly mature archegonium. **B:** Mature archegonium with degenerated canal cells. **C:** Archegonium after opening. **D:** Nearly mature antheridium.

The upper part of the archegonium is called the *neck* and contains the *neck canal cells*. During later stages in archegonial development all cells of the axial row degenerate, except the egg, leaving a canal filled with cell degradation products. This material in the canal swells when water is available. The pressure is released by the sudden pulling back or complete detachment of the cap cells, and the canal material is generally shot free of the archegonial apex (Figure 2·2C). Continuity between the canal and the external medium is thus established and the egg is available for fertilization. The egg degenerates after a period of time if water is not available or if fertilization does not occur.

The antheridium (Figure 2·2D) is located on the surface of, or partially or completely embedded in, gametophytic tissue and, like the archegonium, develops from a single cell. The single cell is emphasized because the complete developmental sequence leading to either antheridium or archegonium formation has been predetermined by the time this cell differentiates from the surrounding vegetative cells. Gamete formation represents the culmination. This developmental system is of particular interest in monoecious plants where both kinds of sex organs are borne on the same plant and, with relatively few exceptions, intersexual structures are uncommon.

The sperm functions to carry the paternal genes to the egg. The whole organization of the sperm is adapted for rapid and efficient mobility through an aqueous medium so that this function can be realized.

The sperms of higher cryptogams are polymorphic; two forms are shown in Figure 2·3. The whiplash flagella are attached at or near the anterior end. Closely associated with the flagellar bases are one or more mitochondria, the "power plants" that presumably supply flagella with energy in a form suitable for flagellar movement. The elongate nucleus containing compacted chromosomes extends nearly the length of the sperm body. Associated with the nuclear material along its length is a fibrillar sheath. The fibers probably are involved in changes in shape of the sperm body. The amount of cytoplasm and nonnuclear cell organelles carried by the sperm, in addition to that associated with the flagellar bases, is variable. In the bryophyte type of sperm the cytoplasmic piece (Figure 2·3A) is lost before sperm entry into the archegonial canal, the amount of extranuclear material carried into the egg thus being minimal. Considerably more cytoplasm, mitochondria, and plastids are carried by the type of sperm shown in Figure 2·3B. The discovery that both mitochondria and chloroplasts carry DNA adds new interest to the study of the process of fertilization in plants, especially as it relates to cytoplasmic versus nuclear inheritance. Additional studies are needed on the formation and structure of the sperm in all

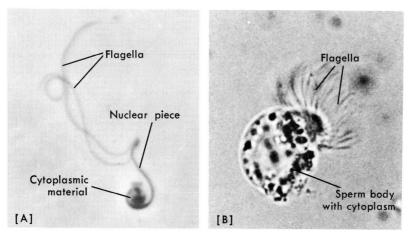

Figure 2·3. Sperm of higher cryptogams. A: Biflagellate sperm of the liverwort *Geothallus tuberosus*. **B:** Multiflagellate sperm of the sphenopsid *Equisetum laevigatum*.

higher cryptogam groups and on the fate of the nonnuclear organelles introduced into the egg cytoplasm.

Radical changes occur in the spermatogenous cells during antheridial development and subsequent sperm formation. The decrease of cell volume during successive mitotic divisions is one of the most noticeable changes, at least at the light microscope level, during antheridial growth. Correlated with this is a great decrease in nuclear volume and in chromosome size. It is not yet clear whether this dramatic diminution in chromosome size during mitoses is a reflection of an actual decrease in DNA content (possibly a change in the number of DNA strands) or the result of DNA compaction. It is evident that everything including nucleolar RNA not directly concerned with the transmission of hereditary characters is removed. The shape of the nucleus also changes, from the usual spherical shape to elongate and narrow with a helical twist. The helical bend to the nuclear piece, and thus to the sperm body as a whole, may be considered to be an adaptation for movement through water.

The mechanism of sperm discharge from the antheridium is variable and no attempt will be made to be encyclopedic in describing it. In some plants the cells at the antheridial apex detach and the sperm mass is extruded through the resultant opening. In others, especially those in which the antheridium is embedded in gametophytic tissue, all cells of the antheridial jacket detach and are extruded along with the sperm mass through a pore in the gametophyte. Several liverworts (such as *Conocephalum* and *Athalamia*) with embedded antheridia exhibit explosive discharge. Here sudden release of pressure at the antheridial apex results in the sperm mass being shot into the air in a visible puff. In these plants air currents aid in the dissemination of sperm over short distances, thereby increasing the chance of outbreeding in populations of monoecious plants.

Fertilization obviously is a critical stage in the life cycle. But not so obvious is the mechanism by which sperm find their way to the archegonium and down the archegonial neck to the egg. Water, as a surface film, is essential for movement of the sperm to the egg. The movement of sperm in tap water or in water containing an unopened archegonium is random. However, it is not random in the presence of an opened archegonium, the sperm swimming toward and collecting at the open neck canal. This directed movement (*chemotaxis*) indicates that a chemical substance, a sperm attractant, emanates from the open archegonium, most likely from the egg. That an open archegonium will attract sperm has been known since 1865, but this interesting phenomenon has been little investigated. Practically all studies have been directed to the chemotactic behavior of sperm to chemicals, but with little specific reference to the archegonium.

Most investigations of sperm chemotaxis have used Pfeffer's (1884) capillary method. In this technique, a capillary tube (10 to 15 mm long and 0.1 to 0.13 mm in diameter) is closed at one end and placed in the solution to be tested. The solution is then placed under a partial vacuum and some of the solution is drawn into the tube, replacing the air. The capillary tube is removed, washed thoroughly, and then placed in a sperm suspension. The test solution diffuses through the open end, establishing a diffusion gradient. A positive result is indicated if the sperm collect at and enter the end of the tube. Problems inherent in the Pfeffer capillary method include sperm entrapment in the tube not related to specific chemotactic attraction and diffusion currents that tend to obscure results. These problems were overcome by Rothschild in 1952 simply by solidifying the test solution in the capillary with 1 per cent agar.

A large number of organic and inorganic compounds have been tested for chemotactic activity and a few of the more noteworthy effective organic compounds are listed in Table 2·1. Note should be made that the data in this table come from studies on relatively few organisms; a study of the chemotactic responses of organisms in each higher cryptogam group has not been done. For example, the data on liverworts come from studies on *Marchantia polymorpha* only.

In addition to its intrinsic interest, a discussion of sperm chemotaxis will serve to remind the student of the specificity that is characteristic

TABLE 2·1
Organic Substances That Attract Higher Cryptogam Sperm [1]

PLANT GROUP	malate[2]	maleate[2]	fumarate[2]	citrate[2]	sucrose	protein
Ferns (several genera tested)	+	+	−	−	−	−
Sphenopsids (*Equisetum*)	+	−	−	−	−	−
Lycopsids:						
Selaginella	+					
Isoetes	+	−	+	−	−	−
Lycopodium	−	−	−	+	−	−
Mosses (four genera tested)	−	−	−	−	+	−
Liverworts (*Marchantia*)	−	−	−	−	−	+

[1] Sperm of hornworts and psilopsids have not been included in chemotactic studies to date.

[2] Included here is the acid form, the monohydrogen form and the doubly ionized form of the molecule.

of biological reaction systems in general. Sperm of most ferns (*Marsilea* is an exception), the sphenopsid *Equisetum,* and the lycopsids *Selaginella* and *Isoetes* exhibit positive chemotaxis in the presence of various salts of malic acid, but they differ in their response to salts of the geometrical isomers maleic and fumaric acid (Table 2·1 and Figure 2·4). Further, it is known that malic acid in solution is represented by three forms: malic acid, the monohydrogen-malate ion (bimalate), and the malate ion (Figure 2·4). Because of the possibility of hydrogen bonding the *cis*-configuration of the monohydrogen-malate ion would be favored. On the other hand, the tendency of the two carboxyl groups of the undissociated malic acid molecule or the doubly dissociated malate ion to repel each other results in the *trans*-configuration of these molecules in solution (Figure 2·4). In 1958 Brokaw presented evidence that sperm of the bracken (the fern *Pteridium aquilinum*) respond preferentially to the monohydrogen-malate ion—a *cis*-compound. This is consistent with the earlier observations that fern sperm react to salts of maleic acid, also a *cis*-compound, but not to its *trans*-

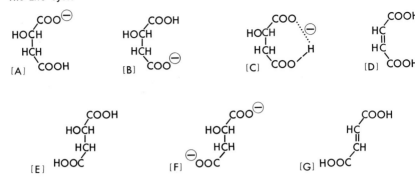

Figure 2·4. Chemotactic substances. A, B: Two forms of the monohydrogen-malate ion in solution, the form shown in **A** is more abundant in solution. **C:** Monohydrogen-malate ion showing possible hydrogen bonding. **D:** Maleic acid, a *cis* compound; **E, F:** Malic acid and the malate ion, respectively; both preferentially in the *trans* form when in solution. **G:** Fumaric acid, a *trans* geometrical isomer of maleic acid.

geometrical isomer, fumaric acid. On the other hand, sperm of the lycopsid *Isoetes* are attracted to salts of fumaric acid and there is evidence that they react preferentially to the malate ion, also in a *trans*-configuration. The results of these and other experiments suggest that sperm not only possess sensory areas that detect specific organic compounds, but that they can also distinguish between *cis*- and *trans*-configurations. (Review at this time the metabolic role of malic and fumaric acids in cell physiology.)

Sperm also have sensory areas for cations. Several cations, such as potassium, calcium, rubidium, and strontium, have chemotactic effects separate from their associated anions. As might be expected from the studies on anions described earlier, sperm in the different plant groups differ in their sensitivity to cations. The interested student should refer to the article by Machlis and Rawitscher-Kunkel (1967) for additional information on gamete attraction in plants, in general, and for the pertinent bibliography.

Sperm chemotaxis remains of considerable theoretical interest, in spite of the general lack of studies during the past fifty years. Our information comes from observations on disappointingly few organisms. Moreover, in vitro studies on sperm chemotaxis will not answer the more basic question of the nature of the in vivo sperm-to-egg attractant. Is there basis for the assumption that organic compounds as widespread in biology as malic acid, sucrose, and protein are identical to chemotactic emanations from the archegonium? We have insufficient information, none of recent origin and most of it confusing. In 1891 Voegler showed that sperm of different species of ferns are attracted to, and have about the same sensitivity to, concentrations of salts of malic acid. However, he also found that the sperm of the several species of these same ferns are not attracted to and do not enter the archegonia of all species tested. In other words, some sperm were attracted to the archegonia of other species; others were not. One might expect that an open archegonium would attract fern sperm indiscriminately if monohydrogen-malate were the main chemotactic substance for ferns in vivo. Somewhat more recently, Showalter (1927) found that the open archegonium of the liverwort *Fossombronia* attracted sperm of other liverworts and even the moss *Funaria*. However, Table 2·1 indicates that moss and liverwort sperm are attracted to chemically dissimilar substances.

It is perhaps redundant to comment that we still have much to learn about sperm chemotaxis. Future investigations should be directed toward the identification of substances coming from the archegonium and the egg itself. Broadly based studies on the origin and evolution of chemotactic systems within the green plant line of evolution should prove to be rewarding.

The Sporophyte and Spore Development

Fertilization and subsequent embryo development (embryogenesis) occur within the venter of the archegonium. The retention of the zygote within multicellular maternal tissue is characteristic of all land plants, but not of the green algae. For this reason the development of multicellular reproductive organs and the retention of the zygote within the female organ are considered to be adaptations for life under terrestrial conditions. The multicellular maternal tissue acts as a buffer, protecting the egg, zygote, and embryo against vagaries of the external environment, especially against desiccation.

The embryo during its early development is achlorophyllose and dependent on the gametophyte for water, dissolved minerals, and organic compounds (especially sugars), and possibly for hormones. Increasing nutritional independence is obtained when chloroplasts develop during later embryogeny, and, except for the bryophytes, complete nutritional independence is achieved when the sporophyte becomes free-living, that is, physically separated from the maternal plant. Except for the bryophytes the sporophyte is dominant in size and longevity and is the phase of growth one normally associates with the word *fern* or *horsetail*.

The sporophyte of bryophytes differs from the preceding forms in its degree of nutritional independence. Like the other higher cryptogams, the young embryo is nutritionally dependent on the gametophyte. Chloroplasts develop during later embryogenesis and photosynthetic capability has been shown in some mosses. However, the sporophyte remains attached to the gametophyte, spatially separated from the soil by haploid tissue. The gametophyte continues to mediate the movement of water and dissolved minerals throughout the life of the sporophyte.

Spore formation (sporogenesis) is the specific function of the sporophyte of interest to us here. Spores of higher cryptogams are highly specialized cells that develop after meiosis and thus are haploid. They give rise upon germination to the multicellular gametophyte. Meiosis and sporogenesis occur within a multicellular structure called a sporangium. The sporangium can be traced in the fossil record back to the Lower Devonian where it is found even on the leafless and rootless plants of this geologic period. Because of its antiquity the sporangium is considered to be one of the basic organs of green land plants. Sporangial form, structure, and position on the sporophyte vary considerably in the higher cryptogams, but the variation will not be described here. In general, the sporangium consists of a multicellular jacket that surrounds a tissue consisting of (usually) two types of cells. One cell type undergoes meiosis, the haploid cell progeny developing into spores; the other cell type, if present, does not undergo meiosis and ordinarily has a nutritive function or aids in spore discharge from the sporangium.

The mature spore consists of a protoplast surrounded by at least two distinct wall layers (Figure 2·5). The innermost layer, adjacent to the protoplast, is called the *intine.* The spore wall layer external to the intine is referred to as the *exine.* The *perine,* present in some spores, is an additional layer external to the exine. The general terms *exine* and *perine* are sufficient for our purposes, but the student should be aware that an elaborate terminology is available to describe specific subunits of the spore coat.

Spores are amazingly resistant to degradation and occur, with excellent preservation of the spore coat, in the geologic record concomitantly with the earliest land plants. The ability of the single cells to withstand degradation is due primarily to the presence in the spore coat of sporopollenin. Sporopollenin, so named because of its widespread occurrence in spores and seed plant pollen, occurs primarily in the exine and the perine (if present). The chemistry of sporopollenin is still poorly understood, this in spite of over forty years of research. A considerable body of evidence suggests that it is a hydrophobic substance chemically related to, but more highly polymerized than, cutin (see Chapter 3). However, Traverse (1968), who studied the exine residue of beet

Figure 2·5. Electron microscope photos of liverwort spores. A: Spore of *Riccardia pinguis.* Note the two-layered spore coat and the abundant food reserve in the cytoplasm. (Fixation with gluteraldehyde-osmium and stained with uranyl acetate; photo courtesy of Dr. Harry Horner.) **B:** Portion of the coat of the mature spore of *Sphaerocarpos texanus.* (Fixation with osmium; photo courtesy of Myrna Steinkamp.)

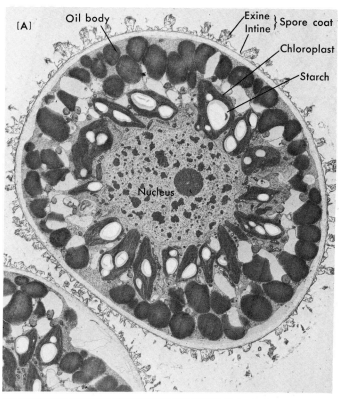

[A] Oil body   Exine }Spore coat
    Intine }
    Chloroplast
    Starch
    Nucleus

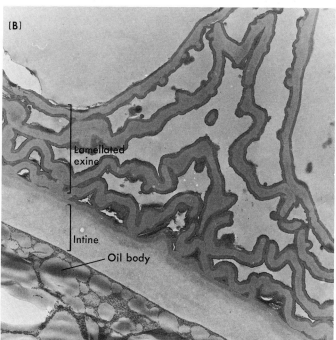

[B] Lamellated exine
    Intine
    Oil body

19

(*Beta vulgaris* L.) pollen, concluded that sporopollenin is a high-molecular-weight polysaccharide with units thought to be similar to those of glucuronic acid. Moreover, there is also evidence for the presence of a lignin (see Chapter 3) component in sporopollenin (Heslop-Harrison, 1968). The study of sporopollenin has been hindered by the complex chemistry of spore and pollen walls. A variety of carbohydrates and waxy substances occur with sporopollenin in the wall, and it has been difficult to obtain sporopollenin that is both chemically cleaned and unaltered by the extraction procedures.

Spores have several functions. They are reproductive units that lead to the dispersal of the organism to new habitats. Especially in the case of annual plants, they are important in the maintenance of the population in the same habitat. Spores often are distributed by wind or water, and many of the variations in spore form and structure appear to be modifications to facilitate dispersal by these forces. Spores are passive during dispersal, and it is entirely by chance that they come to rest and germinate under conditions suitable for the establishment of the organism. Relatively few of the large numbers of spores produced by higher cryptogams give rise to new plants.

The spores also function to carry new gene combinations. Alleles brought together at fertilization are recombined and segregated at meiosis prior to spore formation with the result that the spore may carry a genotype different from that carried by either of the haploid gametes. The greater the genotypic variation in a population of spores, the greater is the likelihood that a genotype will occur that enables a plant to grow in a new or altered environment. Because there is no dominance or recessiveness in the gametophytic growth phase (polyploids are exceptions), rigorous selection occurs during the extended period of vegetative development prior to gamete formation. Mutations and deleterious genes that are expressed during gametophytic growth will be selected for or against during this growth period. The gametophyte is the growth phase during which most of the deleterious genes or gene combinations (often masked in the sporophyte) are deleted from the sexually breeding population. Conversely, those genes, or more correctly codons, that are expressed during sporophytic growth, but are repressed during gametophyte growth, will not be selected against. An example of a spore that apparently carried a new genotype (although this was not proved by requisite genetic studies) deleterious to subsequent gametophyte development became known several years ago during a study of the moss *Physcomitrium*. Several spores were isolated from a single moss sporangium and were placed individually in axenic culture (only a single kind of organism present) on a suitable medium for germination and gametophyte development. All but one plant developed typically following spore germination, the mature or adult stage of growth arising normally from the juvenile phase. (See Chapter 4 for details of moss development.) However, the abnormal plant remained in the juvenile phase and did not produce an adult structure in over a year of culture. Moreover, when the adult structures did appear, they were abnormal. The point is that this plant showing atypical development would not have survived or produced progeny if the spore had germinated in the habitat in which the parent plant had grown. This genotype would have been selected against and deleted from the population. One must keep in mind, however, that although a given genotype might be selected against in one type of habitat, the same genotype might endow the plant with an adaptive advantage under other environmental conditions.

Sporogenesis is a remarkable example of cell specialization. Although the details of spore development differ in several plant groups, especially in regard to the chemistry of the wall layers, the general pattern is similar. By way of example, a single case of spore development will be described briefly (refer to Figure 2·6).

During sporangial development certain cells of the sporogenous tissue differentiate into what are called *spore mother cells* or *sporocytes* (Figure 2·7). As these cells increase in diameter, their cell walls thicken, primarily by the deposition of noncellulosic polysaccharides (containing uronic acids, galactose, mannose, xylose, and arabinose). The spore mother cell then undergoes meiosis and the four haploid cells are generally in a tetrahedral arrangement. Each haploid cell develops into a spore. In the sporogenesis described here a wall layer containing callose (a β-1,3-linked glucan) is deposited nonuniformly around each haploid cell. The pattern of callose deposition is significant in that callose acts as a mold against which the markings of the mature spore coat are cast (Figure 2·6D,E). It has been suggested that the presence of callose additionally serves to isolate the spore protoplast from the influences of the surrounding tissue early in spore development. This suggestion is in accord with the purported role of callose in sealing off or plugging the food-conducting (phloem) tissue of seed plants during certain times of the year.

Two distinct wall layers are sequentially deposited between the callose material and the protoplast. The exine is deposited first, and, in the example discussed here, it consists of a series of lamellae. The outermost lamella is cast against the inner surface of the callose, following its contour. Sporopollenin deposition occurs on a carbohydrate framework early during exine development. Intine deposition occurs during the later stages of spore development. The intine contains cellulose in addition to noncellulosic polysaccharides.

The carbohydrate layer that was deposited around the spore mother cell prior to meiosis and the callose wall material deposited following

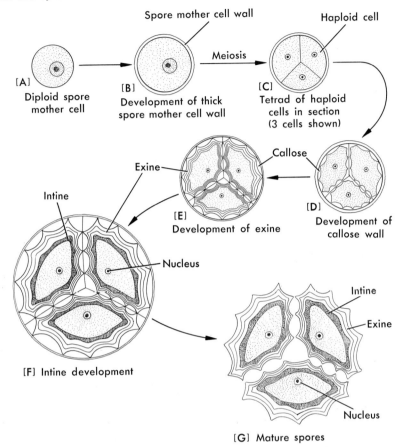

Spore mother cell wall

Haploid cell

[A] Diploid spore mother cell

[B] Development of thick spore mother cell wall

Meiosis

[C] Tetrad of haploid cells in section (3 cells shown)

Callose

Exine

Intine

[E] Development of exine

[D] Development of callose wall

Nucleus

[F] Intine development

Intine

Exine

Nucleus

[G] Mature spores

Figure 2·6. Diagrammatic representation of spore development of a liverwort.

meiosis disappear during later stages in spore development. (In some plants part of the callose wall undergoes modification and forms a spore wall layer external to the exine.) The fate of the carbohydrates in these layers has not been studied to date. Possibly, the carbohydrates are reutilized during later spore development. The spores separate and lie free in the sporangium as a result of the disappearance of the spore mother cell wall that held the tetrad together and the callose material between the spores.

In the higher cryptogams as a group the markings on the external surface of the spore are variable (compare Figures 2·5 and 2·8), but, because they are consistent within a species, the markings, in conjunction with other characteristics, often are of use in species identification. One might think that because of their excellent preservation, fossil spores could be readily assigned to a particular land plant group and

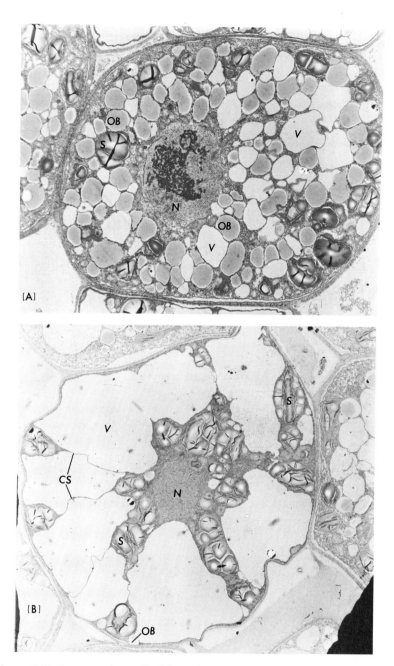

Figure 2·7. Spore mother cell differentiation in the liverwort Sphaerocarpos donnellii. A: Spore mother cell. Note the large number of small oil bodies (OB), small vacuoles (V), starch grains (S) in the chloroplasts, and nucleus (N). **B:** Nutritive (nonmeiotic) cell in same sporangium as **A.** Note large vacuoles (V), starch (S) in chloroplasts, cytoplasmic strands (CS), and almost complete absence of oil bodies (OB). (Fixation with gluteraldehyde-osmium and double-stained with uranyl magnesium acetate and lead citrate.) [Photos courtesy of Mrs. Carole Kelley.]

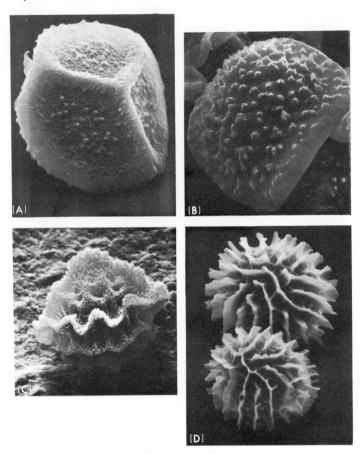

Figure 2·8. Scanning electron microscope photos of spores of three liverworts to show variation in spore coat markings. A: Proximal (inner) spore face of *Riccia campbelliana*. Note the triradiate ridge denoting the surface of contact between the four spores of a tetrad during spore development. **B:** Distal (outer) spore face of *Riccia campbelliana*. **C:** *Asterella californica*. **D:** *Fossombronia longiseta*. (Photos taken with a JSM-2 Scanning Electron Microscope.) [Photos courtesy of Myrna Steinkamp.]

thereby indicate the presence of that plant group in strata even though vegetative plant remains were not preserved. Unfortunately, this has not been possible because identical markings occur on spores of quite different land plant groups.

The chloroplast in the spore mother cells of hornworts and some mosses undergoes changes prior to meiosis, behavior that deserves further attention. The spore mother cells contain a single chloroplast in the organisms under consideration. The chloroplast divides to give rise to four daughter chloroplasts which then move so that they become spaced equidistantly from each other near the cell periphery. The final location of the four chloroplasts indicates the positions of the poles of the future meiotic spindles. Chloroplast division and orientation within the cell thus precede meiosis. Equally interesting are those liverworts (the so-called leafy liverworts or Jungermanniales) in which the spore mother cell becomes four-lobed during spore mother cell differentiation. The diploid nucleus comes to lie in the channel connecting the lobes, where meiosis occurs. After meiosis, one haploid nucleus moves into each lobe and each lobe develops into a spore. Lobing of the spore mother cell in the Jungermanniales and chloroplast division in the hornworts and mosses occur in considerable advance of meiosis.

Changes in content of the vesicles budded off from the Golgi bodies (dictyosomes) are one of the interesting events within the protoplast during sporogenesis. In studies on the liverwort *Riccardia,* Horner, Lersten, and Bowen (1966; see for a comparison with the pattern of spore development described here) found that changes in vesicle content could be correlated with changes in the type of wall material being deposited outside of the plasmalemma. Their work supports a similar conclusion by Ridgway (1965), who studied sporogenesis in a hornwort. The idea that Golgi bodies are involved in the packaging of carbohydrates and glycoproteins for extracellular transport is not new. Their involvement in carbohydrate movement has been shown in animals and flowering plants in elegant experiments using pulse labeling with radioactive carbohydrates. In plants it still has not been determined what specific kinds of carbohydrates are packaged by Golgi bodies. There is evidence to indicate that both the uronic acids and the other noncellulosic polysaccharides are packaged by the Golgi bodies. There is additional evidence (not discussed here) indicating that the Golgi bodies are not involved in the synthesis, intracellular transport, or deposition of cellulose.

The mature spore is a cell of highly specialized function. Sporopollenin present in the outer spore coat not only decreases the rate of water loss by the protoplast, but also acts as a filter to screen out potentially damaging ultraviolet radiation. This is of particular importance to plants that grow in exposed habitats. The protoplast usually contains an abundance of nutrient reserve. Starch is commonly present in plant spores with a rather short life span. The amount of oil present is variable. Plants of xeric habitats ordinarily form spores with an abundance of oils, characteristically unsaturated ones. The presence of unsaturated oils also tends to protect the chromosomes from radiation damage. Spore germination is discussed in Chapter 5.

Apogamy and Apospory

Although the type of life cycle (the sexual life cycle) previously described, in which fertilization and meiosis are essential features, is widespread in the extant higher cryptogams, a significant number of organisms exhibit a life cycle in which fertilization does not occur even though heteromorphic gametophytic and sporophytic generations are present. The sporophyte arises as a direct outgrowth from gametophytic tissue, rather than by fertilization. The origination of sporophytic tissue without the involvement of gametes is known as *apogamy*. Whether the gametophytes that produce apogamous sporophytes additionally give rise to gametes depends on the organisms; some do not produce sex organs, some form only antheridia, and others develop both male and female gametangia. It is of interest that fertilization followed by normal sporophyte development can occur in certain of the plants that also produce apogamous sporophytes. Apogamy in these plants is facultative, sexuality and apogamy presenting alternate pathways to the origin of the sporophyte. Although morphologically similar, the sporophytes have different ploidy levels; the sexually produced sporophyte has twice the chromosome number of the apogamous one.

Spore formation in apogamous plants leads to the re-establishment of the gametophytic growth phase. It will perhaps be surprising to the reader to learn that meiosis occurs prior to spore formation in the majority of apogamous plants studied. Therefore it might be expected that there would be a decrease in chromosome number with time. However, the chromosome number is maintained at the same level by a process in which the genome of the nucleus is doubled (syndiploidy) prior to meiosis. During spore mother cell differentiation, the nucleus undergoes mitosis, but cytokinesis does not occur and the daughter chromosomes are reconstituted within a single nucleus. As a result, homologous chromosomes come to be present within the nucleus and their pairing leads to a normal meiosis with the formation of functional spores. Abortive spores develop within those sporangia in which the chromosome number is not doubled preceding meiosis. Meiosis is a characteristic feature of the apogamous cycle just described even though the spore, sporophyte, and gametophyte all have the same chromosome number. The spore mother cell is the only "2X" cell in the life cycle.

Spore formation is more straightforward in other apogamous plants. Here the chromosome number of the spore mother cell remains constant; syndiploidy does not occur. The nucleus of the spore mother cell undergoes a mitotic division, cytokinesis occurs, and each of the two daughter cells develops into a spore. There is no change in the chromosome number in the entire life cycle, as only mitotic divisions occur. This cycle is referred to as the *ameiotic apogamous life cycle* in order to separate it from the *meiotic apogamous life cycle* described in the preceding paragraph.

Apogamy would seem to provide selective advantage to organisms that grow in habitats having unreliable moisture availability, because its occurrence allows for sporophyte development without fertilization. The influence of environmental conditions on apogamy vis-à-vis sexuality was shown by Freeberg in 1957 during studies on three species of *Lycopodium* (a lycopsid) in axenic culture. He found that sporophytes develop sexually when ample water is available for fertilization, but that apogamous sporophytes develop when there is insufficient water for fertilization. The presence of apogamy would seem to have particular significance to those organisms in which the sporophyte is the dominant, long-lived generation. It is especially widespread in the ferns. Apogamy is not known to occur in bryophytes except in the laboratory, where apogamous sporophytic tissue has been experimentally induced.

Apospory, the capacity of sporophytic tissue to give rise to gametophytes without spore formation, is possible in the higher cryptogams, although the occurrence of this phenomenon under natural conditions is little known. Most of our information comes from observations on laboratory-grown plants where induction of gametophytic outgrowths is usually associated with regeneration from fragments of sporophyte tissue. The regenerants have either the gametophytic or sporophytic form and structure, depending on the cultural conditions under which regeneration occurs or the type of sporophyte tissue used to obtain regenerants.

Regeneration is a fundamental morphogenetic problem in biology in that it relates to determination, embryonization, and totipotency of cells. The ease with which higher cryptogams regenerate, the relatively simple form and structure of these plants, and the ability of the experimenter to control the development pathway (gametophytic versus sporophytic) makes them useful tools in the study of the mechanisms involved in cell differentiation. The student should refer to the 1964 article by Stange for a detailed discussion of regeneration in higher cryptogams because this topic will not be considered in detail here.

Aposporously produced gametophytes are diploid. Therefore the gametes that develop on these plants are also diploid, and fertilization involving two diploid gametes leads to the development of a tetraploid sporophyte. Induction of aposporous outgrowths from the tetraploid sporophyte, in turn, results in the development of tetraploid gamete-producing plants. In this manner it is possible to build up polyploid series; this has been done in some mosses and ferns. The diploid and tetraploid gametophytes characteristically are larger and have more vigorous growth than do their haploid counterparts. They also have increased cell and nuclear volumes. Plants with still higher levels of experimentally induced polyploidy exhibit reduced vigor.

Does any limit exist to the number of chromosomes present within a nucleus as a result of successive cycles of polyploidy? The laboratory experiments previously described would seem to indicate that there is an upper limit to the number of chromosomes tolerated in a nucleus. On the other hand, the very high chromosome numbers characteristic of several of the purported primitive extant higher cryptogams are best explained as resulting from several successive cycles of polyploidy. In the fern genus *Ophioglossum,* for example, diploid, tetraploid, hexaploid, octoploid, and approximately decaploid species are known. Probably the highest chromosome number known in the plant kingdom $2n =$ about 1,260) occurs in this genus. Naturally occurring polyploid series are known in several bryophytes, lycopsids, and ferns. In these cases plants with higher polyploid chromosome numbers, in contrast to those experimentally produced, exhibit vigorous growth; there is no decrease in size or vitality. Stebbins, in a 1966 article in which polyploidy is included in a discussion of evolutionary processes in higher plants, suggests that there is almost no limit to the upward trend of polyploid chromosome numbers, given a sufficiently long time span and genome stabilization between successively higher chromosome levels. It is significant that plant genera with higher polyploid levels also have a long geologic record.

There was the tacit assumption in the preceding discussion that all polyploids arise by apospory. Of course, this is not true; polyploidy can occur by other means. Occasionally, diploid, rather than haploid, spores are produced and the gametophyte resulting from the germination of such a spore is diploid.

Polyploids can also arise following hybridization. Hybridization is the fusion of gametes from genetically unlike parents. If the gametes come from two distantly related parental plants, the sporophyte that develops is usually sterile. This is because the two parental genomes are sufficiently dissimilar so that pairing of homologous chromosomes does not occur during prophase of Meiosis I. The sterile hybrid in this case may be maintained and may even increase in numbers by means of vegetative reproduction. If, at some time, both genomes are duplicated (by a process similar to syndiploidy, mentioned earlier), normal meiosis occurs and the plant then becomes fertile. Polyploidy in this case serves to restore fertility. This type of polyploidy (called *allopolyploidy*) has been implicated in the evolution of certain of the ferns (and many flowering plants).

Polyploid series are common in the higher cryptogams, but they are more common in monoecious plants than in dioecious ones. This fact has led to the suggestion that polyploidy (particularly the type that

results from hybridization) serves to create and maintain genetic variation in organisms that usually undergo self-fertilization. On the other
hand, polyploidy also appears to stabilize the genome, at least with
regard to certain characteristics, because plants with higher polyploids
(such as the psilopsids, *Psilotum* and *Tmesipteris,* the sphenopsid
Equisetum, and some lycopsids and ferns) have retained primitive
characteristics and have long geologic histories.

Vegetative Reproduction

Vegetative reproduction is a means by which plants give rise to new
individuals without going through an alternation of generations. Organisms that have the potential for alternation of generations may also
have the potential to reproduce vegetatively. In some organisms (such
as the liverwort *Marchantia polymorpha*) the structures specialized
for vegetative reproduction and the sex organs are generally produced
at different times of the year. A few plants reproduce entirely by vegetative means; sexual reproduction and spore formation are unknown.

All the vegetatively produced descendants of a single plant are referred to as a clone. Because they are produced by vegetative means,
the plants in a clone are expected to be genetically, and therefore physiologically, identical. In the laboratory, use of clonal cultures is widespread in genetic, developmental, physiological, and biochemical
research where genotypic uniformity is essential.

Vegetative reproduction can occur in either generation when the
higher cryptogams as a single group are considered. However, gametophytic vegetative reproduction is characteristic of bryophytes, whereas
vegetative reproduction of the sporophyte is common in the other
higher cryptogams. Some of the methods of vegetative reproduction
with reference to the generation (haploid or diploid) in which they
occur will now be described.

A structure called a *rhizome* occurs in both the gametophytic (e.g.,
the moss *Polytrichum*) and sporophytic (e.g., many ferns and *Equisetum*) generations. The rhizome, whether haploid or diploid, is an
underground stem from which subaerial stems or leaves arise at inter-
vals (Figure 4·23). Death or breakage of the intervening rhizome
pieces results in the formation of separate, free-living plants. The effi-
ciency of the rhizome in vegetative reproduction is well known to
those persons who have toiled to eradicate colonies of *Equisetum* or
the bracken fern from garden or field. Each fragment left in the soil
gives rise to a new plant.

Sporophytic leaves can also be involved in vegetative reproduction.
An example is the so-called walking fern, *Comptosorus,* that grows in
damp, shaded areas of the eastern and southeastern United States. The

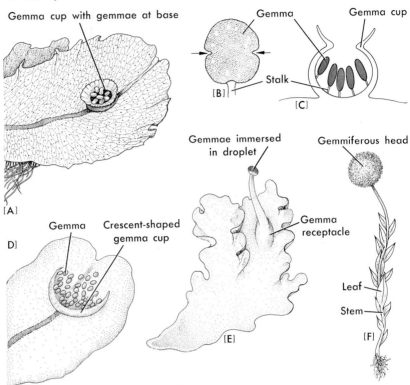

Gemma cup with gemmae at base

Gemma

Gemma cup

Stalk

[B]

[C]

[A]

Gemmae immersed
in droplet

Gemmiferous head

Gemma

Crescent-shaped
gemma cup

Gemma
receptacle

D]

Leaf

Stem

[E]

[F]

Figure 2·9. Gemmiferous structures. A–C: Gemmae structures of the liverwort *Marchantia polymorpha*. **A:** Gemma cup on thallus surface. **B:** Single gemma in surface view; arrows indicate apical notches containing apical cells. **C:** Gemma cup in section showing attachment of gemmae to thallus. **D:** Crescent-shaped gemma cup of the liverwort *Lunularia cruciata*. **E:** Flask-shaped gemma receptacle of the liverwort *Blasia pusilla*. **F:** Gemmiferous head at the gametophore apex of the moss *Aulacomnium*.

tips of the older leaves touch the ground and shoots and roots often develop at these leaf tips. The leaves have a determinate life span and the young plant at each leaf tip becomes independent (it "walks away") when the leaf becomes senescent.

Figure 2·10. Stages in tuber development of the liverwort *Geothallus tuberosus*. A: Cell of a very young tuber. Note the large vacuole, numerous mitochondria, and starch grains within the chloroplasts. (Fixation with osmium; stained with lead citrate.) **B:** Nearly mature tuber cells. Note the numerous black oil bodies, protein bodies, and absence of membrane profiles. (Fixation with gluteraldehyde-osmium; stained with uranyl acetate.) Cell wall (*Cw*), Golgi body (*GB*), starch (*S*), chloroplast (*C*), mitochondrion (*M*), nucleus (*N*), vacuole (*V*), oil body (*OB*), protein body (*P*). [Electron microscope photos courtesy of M. Gene Wolery.]

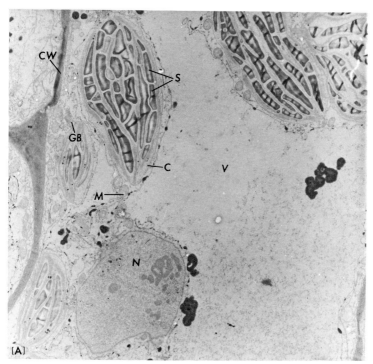

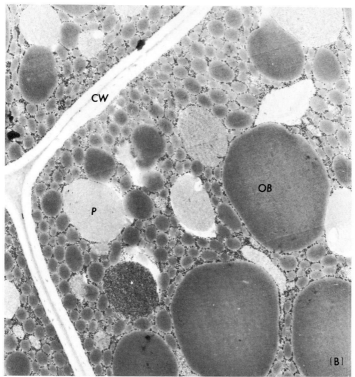

A few ferns have the capacity to develop young plants (plantlets) along the margins of the aerial leaves. These young plants, complete with stems, leaves and roots, develop from meristematic sites on the fern fronds. The plantlets become independent when they detach and fall to the ground.

The gametophytes of some liverworts and mosses develop specialized vegetative reproductive structures called *gemmae*. These generally are multicellular bodies that are small and sufficiently buoyant to be carried by water or wind currents. Gemmae ordinarily develop at the margins of leaves or at the base of specialized flask-, crescent-, or cup-shaped structures (Figure 2·9). They are produced in large numbers and additionally serve to disseminate the species to new habitats.

Tuber formation is also characteristic of a few gametophytes, especially those of liverworts and hornworts. Tubers are stems or portions of stems modified for food storage and dormancy. In some hornworts tubers develop at the margins of the flattened thallus. (Note that in higher cryptogams the term *tuber* is used in a broader sense than in reference, for example, to a potato tuber.) Primarily units of perennation, tubers enable the organism to survive environmental conditions unfavorable for vegetative growth. They additionally serve as units of vegetative reproduction when a plant develops more than one tuber (which is the usual case) and the intervening tissue becomes necrotic.

In a study of tuber development of the liverwort *Geothallus* Wolery (unpublished) and Doyle (1962) found that profound changes occur in cell ultrastructure and in food reserve. The young tuber contains large quantities of starch within the chloroplasts and has numerous membrane profiles (mitochondria, Golgi bodies, and endoplasmic reticulum) characteristic of metabolically active cells (Figure 2·10A). The mature tuber, on the other hand, contains little or no starch; the food reserve is in the form of oil droplets and protein bodies (Figure 2·10B). Moreover, membranous profiles, the morphological manifestation of enzymatic activity, are practically nonexistent in the dormant tuber.

Vegetative reproduction is an alternative method to increase the number of individuals of a species and to enable dispersal of the species to new habitats. The effectiveness of this method is particularly apparent in areas such as the Arctic, where extensive mats of bryophytes exist even though the stringent environmental conditions prevent sexual reproduction. These vegetatively reproducing populations are uniform in form and structure over wide geographic areas. Variation in vegetatively reproducing populations arises through the slow accumulation of random mutations.

Adaptations to Life on Land

IN THE PRECEDING CHAPTER it was pointed out that the basic type of cryptogam life cycle consists of an alternation of a gamete-bearing plant with a spore-bearing one. The gametophytic generation is the dominant growth phase in contemporary bryophytes, whereas the sporophytic generation is dominant in the other higher cryptogams (as well as in seed plants). That organisms in each group have continued to exist approximately from the Devonian period demonstrates that they are well adapted to their particular niche on land. It is the nature of this adaptation that is of interest to us in this chapter.

Water balance has been a problem ever since plants were exposed to the air, and the various structural modifications of the plant body during land plant evolution can be related to adaptation to land. The primitive land plants apparently were already multicellular (as opposed to filamentous). It should be evident that multicellularity leads to an increase in the volume-to-surface-area ratio. Not only are the inner cells of the multicellular structure better protected against desiccation, but multicellularity also makes possible tissue differentiation and specialization. The major modifications in plant structure during adaptation to land are described in the sections that follow.

First, however, note should be made that increasing adaptation to subaerial life does not necessarily mean that land plant evolution is a linear sequence. Many of the modifications to be described apparently originated separately in the major cryptogam groups, and the rate of evolution varied from group to group. Moreover, evolution occurred along different lines in the two growth phases, haploid and diploid. When the higher cryptogams and seed plants are looked at as a single group, we see that the sporophyte is better adapted to life on land. Sporophytes of the early land plants were small and herbaceous; arborescent forms occurred later. With increase in size came an increase in morphological and structural complexity. This increase in size of the diploid plant has been referred to as the ascendancy of the sporophyte during land plant evolution. With the possible exception of the bryophytes, the gametophyte, in contrast, appears to have either remained relatively small or undergone reduction in size and simplification in structure. (We know practically nothing about the gametophytes of fossil plants other than bryophytes, and the gametophytes of most fossil bryophytes look similar to extant forms.)

Thus most of the discussions in the following sections refer specifically to the sporophytic generation.

The Cuticle

Higher cryptogams, and other land plants, would be more vulnerable to desiccation if it were not for the presence of a water barrier in the form of an external coating. This layer, the *cuticle,* contains hydrophobic materials, including cutin and waxes. These substances are secreted by the epidermal cells and form an almost continuous coating over the entire outer surface of the plant (Figure 3·1). Cutin also is found with cellulose in the outer walls of the epidermis. The adaptive

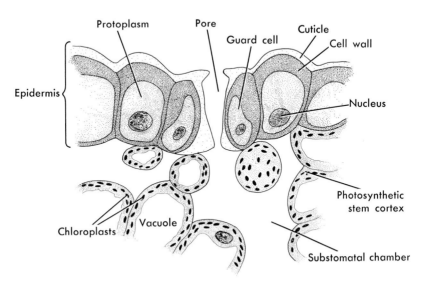

Figure 3·1. Section through a stomatal apparatus in the stem of *Psilotum nudum,* a psilopsid. Note that the cuticle coats the pore surface of the guard cells as well as the outer surface of the epidermis.

significance of the cuticle becomes apparent when xerophytes and hydrophytes are compared. Xerophytes generally have thickened cuticles providing an effective water barrier. On the other hand, hydrophytes possess extremely thin cuticles permeable to both water and gases, or no cuticle at all.

Chemically, the cuticle contains relatively simple substances that are soluble in lipid solvents such as benzene and ether, together with complex polyester compounds that are made soluble only by saponification. Paraffins, aliphatic acids, and aliphatic alcohols are some of the simpler cuticular substances that have been identified. The chemical composition of cutin, a complex polymer made soluble only by saponification, is known only incompletely. From the point of view of this book, it is unfortunate that chemical analyses of cuticular substances have been carried out almost exclusively in the angiosperms, and even here our information comes from studies on relatively few kinds of plants. The presence of the cuticle in higher cryptogams, as in the other plants, is identified by its location, together with its affinity for such dyes for lipids as Sudan IV and Sudan Black B.

Stomata

Stomata or *stomates* (sing. *stoma* or *stomate*) are minute pores in the epidermis that are surrounded by two specialized epidermal cells called *guard cells* (Figure 3·1). The guard cells control the opening and closing of the pore. When open, the pore leads into a substomatal chamber which, in turn, connects with the intercellular spaces of the tissue. Thus the pore gives a direct connection between the air spaces in the interior tissue and the external atmosphere and provides a direct route for the diffusion of gases such as carbon dioxide and oxygen into and out of the tissue. The rate of movement of gases through the pores, primarily a diffusion phenomenon, is much faster than one might suspect and is governed by the physics of diffusion behavior over short distances through suitably spaced small pores. The form, structure, and position of the stomatal apparatus (stoma and guard cells) exhibit considerable variation in the higher cryptogams.

The presence of stomata is one of the most definitive features of land plants, being found on sporophytes in all groups except the liverworts. The development both of a cuticle and of a high volume-to-surface-area ratio favored survival of plants on land. Development of stomata and of an intercellular air space system insured aeration of the tissue and gas exchange with the external environment. However, water vapor is also lost through the stomata (the phenomenon is called stomatal transpiration), and unrestricted water loss can be detrimental to the survival of the plant. The opening and closing of the pore usually is regulated by changes in the turgor pressure of the guard cells relative to the turgor pressure of the other epidermal cells. In general, an increase in turgor pressure in the guard cells results in stomatal opening; a decrease results in closing. Relatively few studies on stomatal physiology of higher cryptogams have been carried out in recent years, in contrast to the situation in angiosperms. A study by Paton and Pearce (1957) indicated that moss stomata close only under conditions of extreme drought and that they reopen when water again becomes available. They also found that, unlike angiosperm stomata, moss stomata are insensitive to changes in light intensity or carbon dioxide concentration. An investigation of stomatal physiology in all the higher cryptogam groups is needed.

The Conducting System

In addition to the cuticle and stomata, the conducting system was an early innovation during land adaptation. Unlike aquatic algae which ordinarily are totally immersed in water, terrestrial plants seldom are in contact with water on all surfaces. The development of a conducting system, involved in the rapid conduction of water from those plant parts with access to water to those parts with a water deficit, seems to be a logical consequence of adaptation to an environment in which parts of plants may be subjected to prolonged desiccation. In fact, growth of any stature seems to have been dependent on the evolution of an efficient conducting system.

The earliest types of water-conducting tissues identified in fossil plants consist of slender strands of elongate cells in the center of the plant axes. These cells, apparently dead in their mature, functional state, possess wall markings (Figure 3·2A–D) characteristic of secondary wall material and are lignified. (Lignin will be discussed later in this chapter.) This type of cell is called a *tracheid*. Tracheids, in turn, are diagnostic of *xylem,* the water-conducting tissue of most land plants. Xylem tissue of the early fossil plants consists entirely of tracheids and the secondary wall thickenings on the tracheids of a plant are all of the same pattern. Xylem elements with annular or helical wall thickenings are common in the early fossil record. Subsequently, scalariform, reticulate, and pitted elements (Figure 3·2) are found. In the more recent fossil record as well as in contemporary higher cryptogams more than one type of element is generally present in the xylem of a single plant. Ordinarily, tracheids that differentiate early during the ontogeny of a plant (during the elongation stage of growth) possess annular or helical wall thickenings. Cell wall extension occurs in those unthick-

Primary wall   Secondary wall   Sieve area

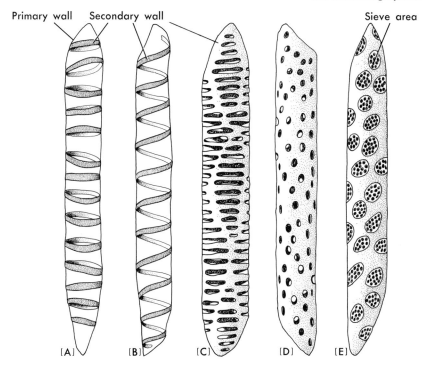

[A]   [B]   [C]   [D]   [E]

Figure 3·2. Conducting elements of higher cryptogams. A–D: Patterns of secondary wall deposition on tracheids. **A:** Annular. **B:** Helical. **C:** Scalariform. **D:** Pitted. **E:** Sieve cell with numerous sieve areas.

ened areas of the primary wall. The differentiation of tracheids with more extensive secondary wall deposition is correlated with the cessation of elongation. However, not all patterns of wall thickenings are found necessarily in a given plant species and there often are transitions of different types of thickening even on the same cell.

It seems unlikely that the most primitive land plants already had tissue as specialized as xylem. Obviously, we do not know, and will never know with certainty, the form and structure of the earliest type of specialized water-conducting tissue. In this connection, mosses are of considerable interest because the sporophytes of these plants possess thin strands of elongate cells, called *hydroids,* of a type simpler than the cells of tracheids. In contrast to tracheids, cells of these hydroids are thin-walled and nonlignified. They are similar to tracheids in being dead at maturity, at least in some mosses. It remains an open question whether these cells in mosses represent conservation of a primitive condition or are the result of simplification (regressive evolution) from a previous tracheidlike state. The total absence of pertinent information in the known fossil record coupled with the paucity of anatomical, ontogenetic, and physiological studies of the conducting system of contemporary mosses preclude a more definitive statement. Whatever the speculation, the hydroids in the central strand of moss sporophytes are, in fact, functional counterparts of tracheids. This has been shown again by Bopp and Stehle (1957), working with the moss *Funaria*. Studying the conduction of water-soluble fluorescent dyes, they found that water was preferentially and rapidly conducted in hydroids, confirming the results of previous investigators.

It seems plausible to suggest that primitive land plants possessed a thin strand of elongate conducting cells placed centrally in the plant axis. These cells were relatively thin-walled, nonlignified, and living in their mature, functional state. Cell death seems to have occurred early in the evolution of water-conducting cells. It should be evident that in cells devoid of protoplasm there is less resistance offered to water movement than in living cells. The localization of secondary wall deposition that resulted in characteristic wall patterns and the association of lignin with cell walls appear to have been subsequent innovations. Even the unthickened wall areas of the tracheid, however, offer measurable resistance to water flow. The most highly evolved type of water-conducting elements is one in which, prior to cell death, portions of the primary cell wall are dissolved in the regions where two conducting cells overlap. A series of open tubes results. Each vertical file is called a *vessel* and the component "cells" are known as *vessel elements*. Although characteristic of angiosperms as a group, vessel elements occur in relatively few contemporary higher cryptogams—in some species of the lycopsid *Selaginella*, in the ferns *Pteridium* and *Marsilea*, and in the sphenopsid *Equisetum*. Vessels are equally rare in the gymnosperms, occurring only in *Gnetum*, a genus of tropical lianes.

A food-conducting tissue is spatially associated with the water-conducting tissue in most higher cryptogams. This tissue is called *phloem* in those plants with xylem. Just as tracheids are characteristic of xylem, *sieve elements* are diagnostic of phloem. Xylem and phloem together constitute the vascular system of the plant body. The term *vascular plants* is a convenient term used to refer collectively to the higher cryptogams (exclusive of bryophytes), the gymnosperms, and the flowering plants.

Sieve cells (Figure 3·2E) are the specific kinds of sieve elements found in phloem of higher cryptogams (and gymnosperms). These cells are elongate, often with tapered end walls, and the primary walls are relatively thick, especially in the later stages of sieve cell differentiation. The highly hydrated walls usually have a pearly luster. There are only a few reports of the presence of lignin in these walls, for example, in the contemporary psilopsid *Tmesipteris*. The presence of differentiated sievelike areas in the cell wall distinguishes sieve cells from other cell types. The sieve areas, usually numerous on end walls where sieve cells overlap, represent a cluster of pores through which extend coarse connecting strands of protoplasm. In some higher cryptogams a cylinder of callose, a β-1, 3-linked glucan, encases each connecting strand in the pore; the callose replaces cellulose in the wall in these areas. The relationship between cell structure and function is clearly shown by sieve cells because the elongate cells with protoplasmic continuity through the sieve areas are well suited for the efficient translocation of dissolved food, such as sucrose, from one part of the plant to another. However, the mechanism of food translocation from one cell to another remains unknown.

Sieve cells, in contrast to tracheids, are living cells with protoplasm. The cells retain their nucleus at maturity, although nuclear size decreases considerably during cell differentiation. In this, sieve cells differ from the mature, enucleate sieve element (called sieve tube elements) of flowering plants. The enucleated sieve tube elements have retained their protoplasm and certain vital functions such as membrane differential permeability. (They are like mammalian red blood cells in this respect.) Apparently, the mechanism of transport of organic materials in phloem is dependent on the presence of living cells. Phloem transport in flowering plants ceases when the stem has been killed; the same is true, presumably, in sieve cell function.

In moss sporophytes the water-conducting tissue is also spatially associated with a (presumed) food-conducting tissue. The food-conducting cells, called *leptoids,* are elongate, relatively thick-walled, and nucleated at maturity. They are not sieve cells, however, in that specialized sievelike areas have not been found. It is probable that the evolutionary progenitors of sieve cells closely resembled the present level of differentiation of leptoids.

The significance of the development of a food-conducting tissue, as well as a water-conducting tissue, during land adaptation can be appreciated when one notes that this tissue has been described in sporophytes representing all groups of the higher cryptogams, except liverworts and hornworts. Food-conducting tissue must have had a long evolutionary history, perhaps as long as that of water-conducting tissue. However, much less is known about the evolution and function of the cells specifically involved in food conduction. This lack of information is due, in part, to the fact that phloem is more poorly preserved in fossil plants than is xylem. Apparently, the presence of lignin makes xylem more resistant to degradation. Because of the lamentable lack of investigations on the physiology, ontogeny, and comparative anatomy (at both the light and the electron microscope level) of leptoids and sieve cells, it is impossible to present a more detailed picture of the form, function, and evolution of food-conducting elements in the higher cryptogams.

Evolution of the Stele

Several innovations together helped solve the immediate problem of desiccation faced by the aerial parts of land plants, among which were the development of the cuticle, an increase in the volume-to-surface-area ratio, and the differentiation of an efficient water-conducting system. An effective gas exchange system, to counter the presence of the cuticular diffusion barrier, was made possible by the development of stomata. During continued adaptation to land, plants increased in size with concomitant increase in complexity of the conducting system. The simple central strand of elongate cells characteristic of many of the smaller, poorly differentiated vascular plants gave way in the larger forms to more complicated conducting systems. A little of the diversity in arrangement of the vascular bundles within a single genus of higher cryptogams, as seen in cross-sectional view, is shown in Figure 3·3 (see also Chapter 4, Diversity).

Plant anatomists and morphologists, impressed by the diversity in vascular bundle arrangement, looked for a unifying concept that would make comparisons of conducting systems and plant structure meaningful. The most useful concept, and the one that is still accepted by many, was suggested in 1886 by van Tieghem and Douliot. They suggested that the primary bodies of vascular plants are basically alike: All vascular plants have a central column called the *stele,* surrounded by the *cortex.* The stele contains the conducting tissue, whether composed of a single strand, a number of strands, or a series of plates. The stele and cortex are delimited by the *pericycle* and *endodermis,* the pericycle being the outermost region of the stele and the endodermis the innermost layer of the cortex (Figure 3·4).

The endodermis is identified histologically by the presence of the *Casparian strip* (Figure 3·5). The strip, named after Caspary, its discoverer, is formed by the localized impregnation of complex polymers into specific areas of the primary wall. There is still no general agreement on the chemistry of the Casparian strip. A lignin reaction has been shown, and cuticularlike hydrophobic substances have also been found. The Casparian strip extends completely around the transverse and radial walls of the endodermal cells. This pattern of impregnation of hydrophobic material insures that movement of dissolved

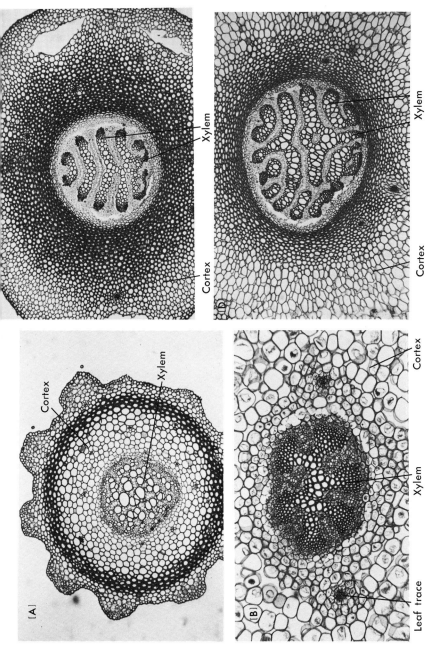

Figure 3·3. Diversity in form of xylem tissue in stems of four species of *Lycopodium*, a lycopsid. A: *L. cernuum.* **B:** *L. lucidulum.* **C:** *L. annotinum.* **D:** *L. clavatum.*

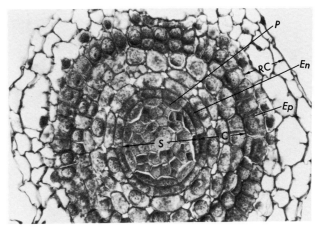

Figure 3·4. Cross section of a root of *Equisetum hyemale*, a sphenopsid. The section was cut immediately behind the root apex (see Figure 3·10) and primary tissue differentiation is incomplete. Future cortex (C), endodermis (*En*), epidermis (*Ep*), pericycle (*P*), root cap (*RC*), stele (*S*).

solutes from the cortex into the stele is subject to the regulatory activity of the living endodermal cells. An endodermis is common in the vascular cryptogams, but its relationship to function is not well established. Instead of an endodermis, the innermost layer of the cortex of some young flowering plant stems consists of a *starch sheath,* the cells of which contain numerous starch grains and lack the Casparian strip. Because it is found where an endodermis would occur if it developed, the starch sheath is considered to be homologous with the endodermis. The reason for introducing the starch sheath at this time is that a similar starch-containing tissue, also called a starch sheath, has been described in the stem of some moss gametophytes (e.g., *Polytrichum*). It is important to note, however, that the starch sheaths of mosses and of flowering plants are not homologous structures; the starch sheath of mosses belongs to the haploid generation, whereas that of flowering plants belongs to the diploid.

The concept of the stele was later formulated as the Stelar Theory. In simple terms, the Stelar Theory interprets the primary structure of the shoot and root as being fundamentally similar. In each organ a central cylinder, the stele, is enveloped by the cortex. The value of the Stelar Theory as a unifying concept stimulated a considerable amount of comparative research and a voluminous literature resulted, with a wealth of information concerning gross anatomy of plant axes, the ontogenetic origin of the endodermis and of the tissues of the stele, and changes in stelar form during plant growth. Moreover, acceptance of the Stelar Theory gave meaning to attempts to interpret phylogenetically the varied types of vascular arrangements.

A stele that contains a solid central strand of xylem is called a *protostele*. This type of stele, of frequent occurrence in the early land plants and in the roots and shoots of contemporary higher cryptogams, is considered to be phylogenetically the most primitive. A *siphonostele* contains xylem in the form of a tube, the central region of parenchymatous cells being called *pith*. In transverse section, the xylem of the tube may appear as a complete ring of tissue or it may be interrupted so that in extreme cases the ring is made up of a series of discrete areas of xylem. There is evidence, from fossil and extant plants, that the siphonostele developed phylogenetically from protostelic types within each group of vascular cryptogams. The variety of other stelar forms considered variants of protosteles or siphonosteles will not be described here.

Xylem is more than a water-conducting tissue in aerial plant parts. It also is supportive and there is a striking correlation between stelar form and plant size, implying a functional relationship. Although there are exceptions, the protostele is characteristic of the smaller vascular cryptogams, both fossil and extant, and of roots even in those plants in which the aerial parts are nonprotostelic. The siphonostele occurs most commonly in, but is not restricted to, plants with larger aerial axes. Moreover, stelar structure can change during plant growth. For example, the stem of a young fern plant often is protostelic, but a

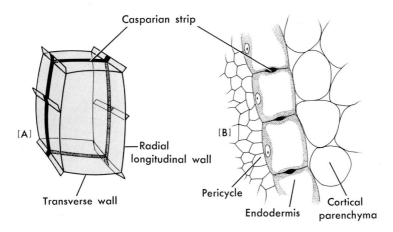

Figure 3·5. The endodermis. A: Endodermal cell showing location of the Casparian strip on the radial longitudinal and transverse walls. **B:** Appearance of the Casparian strip as viewed in cross section of the tissue. Note air spaces between the cortical parenchyma cells.

siphonostele differentiates during later growth when stem size has increased. It has been suggested that this correlation between size and structure is usually related to supportive demands on the plant. A hollow cylinder or a series of longitudinal strands in the shape of a tube offer greater structural support than does a single solid column of comparable diameter. Some of the changes in stelar form, then, can be related to ontogenetic as well as phylogenetic changes in plant size.

Phylogenetic change in stelar form is also correlated with the development of leaves and branches with associated leaf gaps and branch gaps in the vascular tissue of siphonostelic plants. These gaps are areas in which parenchyma cells differentiate instead of xylem cells. This results in the continuity of parenchyma cells between cortex and pith.

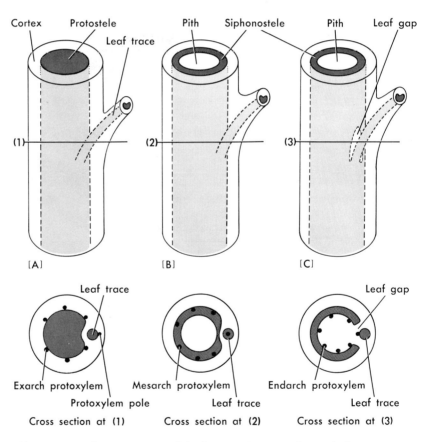

Figure 3·6. Stelar anatomy and leaf gaps. A: Protostele, no leaf gaps present. **B:** Siphonostele, no leaf gaps present. **C:** Siphonostele, with leaf gaps.

The occurrence of gaps in siphonostelic plants is dependent on the amount of xylem that extends from the main axis to a lateral organ (whether leaf or branch) together with the pattern of differentiation of the xylem of the main axis (Figure 3·6). Xylem differentiation in a plant can be separated into two somewhat overlapping phases. *Protoxylem* differentiates early, before and during the cell enlargement phase of plant growth, whereas *metaxylem* differentiates near or after completion of the enlargement phase. Protoxylem differentiates as a series of small strands (called protoxylem poles when viewed in cross section) and is identified histologically by the small diameter of the cells. Protoxylem poles may occur (1) at the outer margin of the xylem, toward the cortex (*exarch* pattern of differentiation); (2) at the inner margin, toward the pith (*endarch*); or (3) somewhere in between, surrounded by metaxylem (*mesarch*). At least one protoxylem strand, with associated metaxylem, extends from the stele through the cortex and out into a leaf or branch. Leaf and branch gaps occur when the protoxylem poles are on the pith side of the stele. (Possible exceptions occur in the sphenopsids, but inadequate space precludes a discussion of these forms.) Gaps may or may not develop when the protoxylem poles are on the cortical side of the stele or are surrounded by metaxylem. For example, only a small amount of metaxylem accompanies the protoxylem from the stele into the leaves of fossil and extant siphonostelic lycopsids, causing no break or gap in the vascular tissue (Figure 3·6B). On the other hand, branch gaps do occur in these plants and are the result of a much larger amount of metaxylem accompanying the protoxylem into the branch.

The protoxylem poles are located at or near the periphery of the xylem in protostelic plants. This position, coupled with the lack of pith, makes it impossible for leaf or branch gaps comparable to those of siphonostelic plants to develop.

Secondary Growth

The types of steles just described form the basic conducting system of plants and result from the differentiation of cells produced at the growing tips. The tissues formed from the differentiation of these cells are called *primary tissues*, for example, *primary xylem* and *primary phloem*. The development of an efficient water-conducting system made possible an increase in stature of the aerial parts of land plants, and an increase in height gives a significant advantage in competition for light. Plants entirely composed of primary tissues are obviously limited in size by the rigidity of the primary vascular and associated supportive tissues. The phylogenetic origin of secondary growth made possible an increase in plant dimension to tree size, a possibility exploited in most land plant groups. A few plants (notably the palms and tree ferns) attain tree dimensions with primary tissues only.

Secondary growth, resulting in increase in girth, was made possible by the phylogenetic development of two distinct cambia, the *vascular cambium* and the *cork cambium*. Ordinarily, the vascular cambium originates during ontogeny from a band of thin-walled cells located between the primary phloem and primary xylem. Mitotic divisions of these cells produce more xylem, *secondary xylem* or wood, on the inside of the band and more phloem, *secondary phloem,* on the outside. The place of origin of the cork cambium is variable, but is usually near the epidermis. The tissues formed from the cork cambium are collectively called *periderm,* a protective tissue that replaces the epidermis when it is sloughed away during increase in girth of the plant axis. Cells external to the cork cambium differentiate into a tissue generally called *cork*. Prior to cell death the walls of cork cells usually are impregnated with *suberin,* a complex hydrophobic polymer related to epidermal cutin, and lignin. The presence of suberin forms an effective diffusion barrier against water loss.

The preponderance of small, poorly differentiated land plants characteristic of the Lower Devonian gave way, by late Devonian, to arborescent forms. Lycopsid and sphenopsid forest trees were a feature of the Carboniferous. Evidence from the fossil record supports the contention that the two cambia, or lateral meristems, arose independently in each vascular plant group. Moreover, although the cambia have similar function in each group, the details are variable. In the arborescent lycopsids, for example, wood production was minimal; most of the increase in girth, and support, was due to massive periderm production. This periderm was not corklike and apparently remained alive for an extended period of time.

Examination of early fossil land plants reveals that the cambium apparently did not develop prior to the phylogenetic development of leaves and apical dominance, that is, not until plants began to look much as they do today. The apparent relationship between the presence of apical dominance and cambial induction is of special significance in that they both are controlled by auxin, one type of plant hormone. (Refer to the book by Torrey in this series for a more extensive discussion of plant hormones and the hormonal control of plant growth and development.)

Arborescent lycopsids and sphenopsids with secondary growth flourished in the Carboniferous, but disappeared soon thereafter. Contemporary forms are herbaceous. If size gives a selective advantage in competition for light, why did not these forms survive? The answer is not known. One suggestion is that the treelike habit of growth, in general, with the resulting production of perennial plants, is of selective advantage only during times of climatic and geologic stability. Under conditions of rapid change, however, the herbaceous habit is favored, the survival value being related to the faster rate of reproduction. There is ample evidence in the geologic record of great climatic changes in the late Paleozoic and early Mesozoic, changes which the arborescent vascular cryptogams apparently were unable to survive. On the other hand, arborescent gymnosperms, with their greater production of secondary xylem, did survive.

Lignin

Lignin occurs in all groups of vascular plants and its presence is correlated with the deposition of the secondary wall. It characteristically is found in the walls of supportive elements (tracheids, vessel elements, and fibers) in land plants in general, but in the higher cryptogams lignin often is additionally associated with other secondarily thickened walls such as those of the epidermis, endodermis, and periderm. Although lignin occurs throughout the wall, it is present in greater concentration in the middle lamella and the primary wall. Studies utilizing C^{14}-labeled precursors have shown that lignin, once deposited, is not reutilized by the plant. It seems to be an end product of metabolism. Moreover, it is metabolized only with difficulty by microorganisms. This in large part accounts for the widespread preservation of lignified tissue in the geologic record.

Lignin is a complex phenylpropanoid polymer, composed of derivatives of the aromatic amino acids, phenylalanine, and tyrosine. In fact, land plants, particularly the vascular plants, accumulate a wide variety of phenylpropanoid derivatives; the flavonoids are another example. Lignin is of additional interest in that it is one of the few secondary metabolites that has been assigned a definite role in plant evolution. Lignin is impregnated within the cell walls and there is evidence that it is chemically combined with the noncellulosic wall components. The presence of lignin better enables the plant to resist compression. Investigations have shown that there is generally a close correlation between the compressive force generated by the mass of the plant and its lignin content. The greater the mass, the greater the amount of lignin present in the walls. Thus the capacity for lignification has been implicated in the increase in size of the vascular plant body during land plant evolution.

Speculations about the phylogenetic origin of lignin center on the possibility that lignification represents one method by which phenolic by-products of land plant metabolism are detoxified. Elimination of toxic waste products in aquatic plants represents no great problem because they can diffuse into and be carried away by the surrounding medium. Retention and accumulation in tissues of land plants, however, would be injurious unless the waste products were detoxified. In the case of lignin it is suggested that the occurrence of chance mutations ultimately led to the conversion of phenolic metabolic by-products into an insoluble form and to their deposition in plant cell walls. Formation of ligninlike compounds was of distinct selective advantage in that it supported the evolution of more massive plant bodies in a subaerial environment. Thus lignification later became essential to plant development. It is pertinent to note that land adaptation by animals was dependent on the evolution of organ systems to take care of metabolic by-products. Animals excrete these waste products; plants retain them within their tissues, generally within vacuoles or in cell walls. The apparently obligate dependence of lignification upon secondary wall deposition has not been satisfactorily explained.

The almost complete absence of lignin in bryophytes needs brief comment. Prior to 1969 lignin had been reported in only three bryophytes (the liverwort *Jungermannia* and the mosses *Sphagnum* and *Polytrichum*), but in no case was it associated with conducting tissue. Moreover the lignin of these plants is quite dissimilar in the ultraviolet absorption spectrum to lignin of vascular plants. On the other hand, Siegel (1962) reported that of the five bryophytes (including the moss, *Polytrichum*) he tested, all were similar to vascular plants in their ability to convert eugenol (a lignin precursor) into lignin. The type of lignin produced was spectroscopically similar to that of vascular plants.

Evidence for the presence of lignin in the gametophytic stems of two mosses, *Dawsonia* and *Dendroligotrichum,* was presented by Siegel in 1969. Both these plants occur in, but are not restricted to, New Zealand, range from thirty-five to fifty-five centimeters in length, and possess lignin with many characteristics similar to those of flowering plant lignin. Localization of lignin within the stem tissue was not reported in Siegel's paper nor was the sporophyte tested for the presence of lignin. Lignin has not been found to occur naturally in gametophytic stems of smaller mosses, including *Polytrichum*, a relative of *Dawsonia* and *Dendroligotrichum.* However, the above studies show that bryophytes have the ability to synthesize lignin. The occurrence of substantial quantities of lignin in stems of tall mosses further supports the suggested role of lignin in increased plant stature during land plant evolution.

The discovery of the leafless and rootless vascular plants (e.g., *Rhynia* and *Horneophyton*) in Devonian strata of Scotland was, and remains, of considerable theoretical interest, because it indicated that the leaf and the root are not necessarily basic organs of vascular plants. Moreover, a growing body of evidence indicates that the distinction between stem and leaf becomes less and less pronounced as one compares older and older fossils in each phylogenetic line of vascular plants. This has led to a re-evaluation of our organographic concepts. One current line of thought is that the "leaves" of the psilopsids, lycopsids, sphenopsids, and ferns are not homologous structures, that they evolved independently in each major phylogenetic line of vascular cryptogams. Because the leaves in the plant groups have similar functions, convergent evolution resulted in the similarities in leaf form and structure. This raises the semantic problem of whether the structures identified as leaves should all be called leaves, if they are not homologous. However, we shall continue to use this term throughout the book rather than a new term for leaflike structures in each phylogenetic line. The remainder of this section will describe (1) the probable progenitor of leafy vascular plants and (2) two current theories concerning the phylogenetic development of leaves.

Based on the evidence from the fossil record, it is reasonable to suggest that the type of land plant that subsequently gave rise to leafy plants had the following form and structure: The plant possessed erect, probably cylindrical aerial axes, most likely with dichotomous branching. In addition, the erect axes, with cuticle and stomata, were vascularized by a thin protostele. There is no incontrovertible evidence from the fossil record or from extant plants to indicate that sporophytic leaflike structures evolved before the development of xylem and phloem. In this connection, it is of interest that the nonvascular sporophytes of all bryophytes are leafless (although it should be noted that leaves do occur in the gametophytic generation of many).

The influence of the discovery of the leafless and rootless Devonian psilopsid *Rhynia* (Figure 3·7) on our thinking is apparent from the preceding description. The simple form and structure of this plant, described from the Rhynie cherts of Aberdeenshire, Scotland, lends itself well to phylogenetic speculation. It should be pointed out that *Rhynia* existed contemporaneously with plants with leaves, and that *Rhynia* was but one genus of a rather large and diversified flora of relatively undifferentiated higher cryptogamous plants in existence in Devonian times. However, this does not controvert the argument, because it is not suggested that leafy plants evolved from *Rhynia*, but from plants with many *Rhynia*like characteristics.

Two contrasting, but not necessarily mutually exclusive, theories

Figure 3·7. Reconstruction of *Rhynia gwynne-vaughanii*, a Devonian psilopsid.
Note terminal sporangia, lack of differentiation into stem and leaf, and absence of
roots. [Courtesy of the Field Museum of Natural History, Chicago, Illinois.]

concerning the phylogenetic origin of leaves, the Enation Theory and
the Telome Theory, will be discussed here. The concept of the *de novo*
origin of leaves is basic to the Enation Theory, whereas the Telome
Theory is based on the concept that leaves developed by modification
of pre-existing structures.

According to the Enation Theory, the first major step in the phylogenetic development of leaves was the outgrowth of a protuberance, or
enation, from a previously naked surface. The subsequent evolution of
leaves from enations involved increase in size with concomitant morphological and anatomical differentiation. Figure 3·8 shows how
enation leaves might have developed from a leafless progenitor. The

most significant step was the formation of the enation itself. The development of a rudimentary leaf trace continuous with the vascular tissue of the stem and extending to the base of the enation occurred later. Extension of the leaf trace as an unbranched midvein from leaf base to apex was the next evolutionary advance. Note that the series represents a typological series only; the plants chosen illustrate major steps in the theoretical development of leaves from enations. Although they existed early in the vascular plant fossil record, there is no intent to suggest that any one of the plants gave rise to any of the others in the series.

In an early statement, Bower (1908) suggested that leaves of all land plants are enation leaves, derived phylogenetically from enations. According to this view, leaves from the first were minor appendages on the stem. In some plant groups, such as the lycopsids, leaves remained small; in ferns, however, considerable leaf enlargement occurred. Perhaps it is pertinent to note in this connection, as did Bower, that during their ontogeny leaves of contemporary plants arise as enations at the shoot apex and that the first few leaves of plants are generally smaller and anatomically simpler than subsequent leaves.

The availability of additional information, especially that obtained from the study of early fossil plants, resulted in a re-evaluation of the Enation Theory and was followed by a restatement by Bower in 1935. Bower then recognized two general types of leaves, *microphylls* and *megaphylls*, and suggested that each type resulted from a different pathway in leaf evolution. Only the microphyll was considered to have evolved from enations. As the name implies, the microphyll often is a small leaf with a single, generally unbranched vascular midvein that extends from leaf base to apex. Divergence of the leaf trace from the

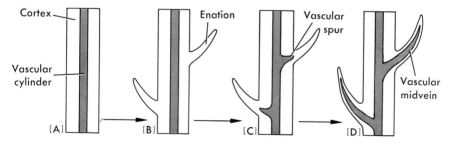

Figure 3·8. Typological series to show hypothetical evolutionary development of microphylls from enations, as typified by Devonian plants. A: *Rhynia,* no enations. **B:** *Psilophyton,* primitive enations. **C:** *Asteroxylon,* vascular trace extends through the cortex to the base of the enation. **D:** *Drepanophycus,* vascular trace extends well into enation.

vascular cylinder is not associated with a corresponding leaf gap, the microphyll being usually found on protostelic plants.

The restricted application of the Enation Theory, that only microphylls developed phylogenetically from enations, is still accepted by many plant morphologists. Leaves or leaflike structures that look morphologically and anatomically as if they might have developed from enations occur in the lycopsids and psilopsids. Although often called microphylls, it remains to be determined in the future whether these structures are, in fact, enation leaves.

The Telome Theory contains the concept that leaves evolved by the phylogenetic specialization of aerial branch systems. Many of the premises were developed originally in an attempt to explain the origin of the fern megaphyll, usually a large leaf with complex venation and ordinarily associated with a well-defined leaf gap in the vascular cylinder. The megaphyll generally is found on siphonostelic plants.

The sequence in leaf development is shown diagrammatically in Figure 3·9. The leafless progenitor probably consisted of a dichotomously branched aerial system in which branching occurred in more than one plane. One of the first major steps in the evolution of the leaf was the differentiation of a main axis bearing dichotomously branched lateral units. This presumably occurred by the occasional unequal development of the two axes resulting from a dichotomy, one axis developing strongly and surpassing the other. Referred to as *overtopping,* this process resulted in the dominance of certain branches (presumptive stems) over others (presumptive leaves). Fossils of Devonian plants which exhibit unequal development of sister axes are known.

The flattening, or *planation,* of the branched lateral unit was the next major step in foliar evolution. The final process consisted of de-

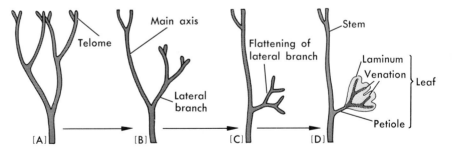

Figure 3·9. Evolutionary development of megaphylls according to the Telome Theory. A: Primitive land plant with branching in three planes. **B:** Overtopping, one axis becoming dominant. **C:** Planation or flattening of the lateral branch system. **D:** Webbing of the lateral branch, resulting in the formation of a leaf with petiole, lamina, and an open dichotomous venation system.

velopment of tissue between the individual members of the lateral branch units, forming a flat leaf lamina characterized by open dichotomous venation. This step in leaf development is referred to as *webbing*.

The German botanist Walter Zimmermann incorporated the preceding processes into his widely applied Telome Theory. (The student should refer to his 1952 and 1965 articles for an expanded discussion of the Telome Theory.) The term *telome* is used to describe the prototype of both axial and lateral organs. According to Zimmermann, the most primitive vascular plants were composed of a system of telomes, and the phylogenetic development of leaves occurred by the processes of overtopping, planation, and webbing of telomic branch systems as previously described. The fusion of separate telomes represents the final critical step in leaf development.

Studies on a large number of fossil ferns lead to the conclusion that there is now no reasonable doubt that fern megaphylls developed from telomic branch units. The fossil record indicates that sphenopsid leaves probably evolved from small lateral, and presumably telomic, branch units. On the other hand, it is striking that the oldest known lycopsids already possessed helically arranged leaves, each with an unbranched vascular midvein. Whether they evolved from enations or from telome-like units remains to be decided. Likewise, the phylogenetic origin of psilopsid leaves is not resolved. There are plant morphologists who interpret these foliar appendages as structures reduced from a small telomic branch unit, whereas others postulate an enation origin.

The Root

Roots have two principal functions: anchorage of the plant to the substrate and absorption of water and mineral ions. Roots lead an active subterranean existence, continuing to grow throughout the life of the plant. The forward growth of the root through the substrate means that the plant continually comes in contact with new sources of water and mineral ions needed for plant growth and development.

The root tip is actually pushed through the substrate during growth. Cell elongation occurs immediately behind the meristematic zone of the root tip. Protection of the meristematic zone from mechanical damage during root elongation is accomplished both by the physical presence of a root cap (Figure 3·10) and the secretion of large amounts of mucilage from the root cap surface. The root cap is one of the definitive morphological features of the root.

Roots are also characterized by the place of origin of lateral branch, or secondary, roots. Lateral branch roots have an endogenous origin;

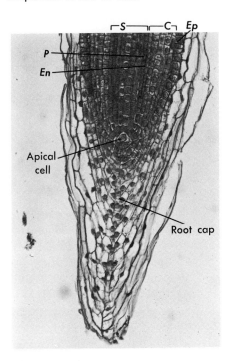

Figure 3·10. Longisection of the root of *Equisetum hyemale* (a cross section of a similar root is shown in Figure 3·4). Primary tissue differentiation is incomplete. Note particularly the large root cap and the distinct apical cell. Cortex (C), endodermis (En), epidermis (Ep), pericycle (P), stele (S).

they develop from pericycle cells that are adjacent to the protoxylem poles. (Lateral branches of the shoot have an exogenous origin, developing from epidermal and hypodermal cells.) Because of its deep-seated origin the root primordium must grow laterally through the endodermis, cortex, and epidermis before it penetrates the substrate.

The growth of roots within tissue of the same plant is more dramatic in many ferns (especially in tree ferns) and in *Lycopodium*. In these plants roots are continually initiated behind the shoot apex (these are called adventitious roots because they develop from nonroot tissue), and they grow for considerable distances down through cortical tissue of the stem before they grow out into the substrate. The root meristem is covered by a root cap during this period of growth and the tissue in the pathway of the elongating root is destroyed. In tree ferns the increase in girth of the stem with age is due to the continued initiation of adventitious roots behind the shoot apical meristem, followed by their downward growth through the cortical tissue; a vascular cambium is absent. Thus roots in these plants additionally serve to support the aerial portion of the plant.

The phylogenetic origin of roots from stemlike structures can be inferred from evidence in the fossil record. Many of the early Devonian land plants lacked roots; here anchorage and mineral ion absorption were accomplished by dichotomously branched, underground stems. The stems of some of these early land plants penetrated the soil for considerable distances and were quite rootlike in general appearance and function. However, there is no evidence for the existence of a root cap. Thus roots, like the megaphyllous leaf described in a previous section, are considered to be modified stems. Specialization of the underground stem into its present form and structure is considered to have occurred in later geologic time and have been of selective advantage to the functioning of this underground plant part.

Homospory, Heterospory, and the Seed

The evolution of the seed is the final topic to be discussed in this chapter. A seed (see Figure 3·11) is generally defined as a mature or ripened ovule containing an embryo. An *ovule,* in turn, is an unopened sporangium surrounded by integumentary tissue of some sort and containing a female gametophyte. Because the earliest land plants did not form seeds, it is assumed that the seed is an evolved structure. Seed formation is an important adaptation to life on land in that it frees the plant of the need for water in order for fertilization to occur.

The sporangium, one of the basic organs of land plants, is the structure in which meiosis occurs and spores develop. Plants with spores that are all morphologically alike are called *homosporous* (or isosporous) plants. Upon germination, spores of homosporous plants give rise to gametophytes that usually have an extensive vegetative development.

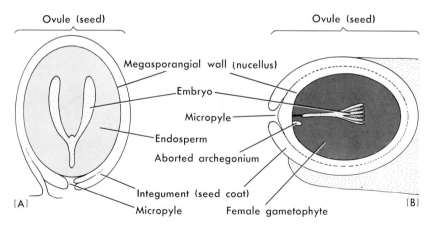

Figure 3·11. Developing seeds of an angiosperm (A) and a gymnosperm (B). A seed is a mature ovule containing an embryo and the protective seed coat is derived from integumentary tissue. Endosperm is nutritive tissue in angiosperms; the female gametophyte is nutritive tissue in gymnosperms.

The gametophytes develop outside of the spore coat and therefore are *exosporic* in their development.

Each class of higher cryptogams has some homosporous representatives. All the plants with monoecious gametophytes are homosporous. These gametophytes have relatively extensive vegetative growth and are generally capable of self-fertilization (Figure 3·12). Because the sporophyte that results from self-fertilization will be homozygous for every gene in the genome, one might expect that, because of the accumulation of random mutations, repeated inbreeding could have a deleterious effect on the long-term survival of the organism. Klekowski and Baker (1966) make note of the high incidence of polyploidy in the homosporous vascular cryptogams, and they suggest that since polyploidy increases gene redundancy, genes would be able to mutate

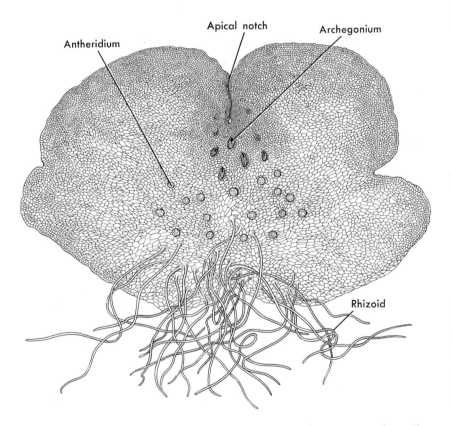

Figure 3·12. Lower surface of the gametophyte of a homosporous fern. The archegonial necks of this monoecious plant point toward the antheridia, an apparent adaptation for self-fertilization. [Redrawn from William H. Brown, *The Plant Kingdom*, Boston: Ginn and Company, 1935.]

and to take on new functions without detriment to the physiology of the organism. Thus polyploidization might be of selective advantage as a means of maintaining the genetic variability in predominantly self-fertilizing plants.

In some monoecious plants the opportunity for self-fertilization is decreased by the timing of gametangial initiation. Depending upon the organism, antheridial or archegonial initiation begins first, although there is generally a period of time during which mature gametangia of both types occur on the same plant. A different system that results in a high proportion of heterozygous sporophytes in monoecious plants is found in the bracken fern *Pteridium aquilinum*. Here less than 20 per cent of the gametophytes are capable of giving rise to homozygous sporophytes; the others require cross-fertilization for normal sporophyte development to occur. It is not known why some gametophytes are able to give rise to homozygous sporophytes and others are not. Although other species of monoecious ferns studied have been found to be completely self-compatible, the frequency of inbreeding in nature by these homosporous plants has not been determined.

The formation of spores of two dissimilar sizes is characteristic of *heterosporous* plants. Each type of spore is formed in a separate sporangium, but both kinds of sporangia may occur on the same plant (Figure 4·20B). One kind of sporangium, the *microsporangium,* produces a large number of spores called *microspores.* Upon germination, microspores give rise to male gametophytes, or microgametophytes. The other kind of sporangium, the *megasporangium,* forms *megaspores,* spores that are usually larger than the microspores. Megaspore germination leads to the development of the female gametophyte, or megagametophyte. The extent of vegetative growth of both female and male gametophytes of heterosporous plants is reduced markedly relative to the extent of growth of the gametophytes of homosporous plants. Heterosporous plants have gametophytes that complete most or all their development within the confines of the spore coat; they have *endosporic* gametophytes. Today, heterosporous representatives occur in the Lycopsida and in the Pteropsida (as well as in the Spermopsida); fossils of heterosporous lycopsids, sphenopsids, and pteropsids are known.

The facts that the sporangium of heterosporous plants normally forms spores all of one type, either mega- or microspores and that both sporangial types may be formed on the same plant indicate that the sex of the spore is determined not during meiosis but during sporangial development. In these plants it appears likely that microspores and megaspores carry the genetic potential for both antheridium and archegonium formation. The fact remains, however, that antheridia only are initiated on microgametophytes and archegonia only on megagameto-phytes. The long-term control of sex expression in these heterosporous plants appears to be set irreversibly by the sporangial environment in which the spores develop. The time at which control of the developmental pathway is set is variable. In *Isoetes,* a lycopsid, control of gametophytic sex expression occurs during the differentiation of the spore mother cells; in *Selaginella,* also a lycopsid, control occurs after spore mother cell differentiation but prior to meiosis; and in the water fern *Marsilea,* control of the developmental pathway occurs immediately after meiosis. Some evidence suggests that nutrition plays a role in the control of gametophytic sex expression. However, an understanding of the control of developmental pathways must be sought at the level of differential gene repression and derepression, and this still remains to be studied in sporangial development. (A more detailed discussion of the problems associated with the origin of heterospory can be found in the article by Sussex, 1966.)

In the preceding discussion homospory and heterospory were defined in morphological terms. Homosporous plants form spores that are of identical size, whereas heterosporous plants form spores of two dissimilar sizes. A description of function was purposefully omitted from the definition, partly because of the problem this would raise with respect to fossil plants in which spore function could not be tested. However, a number of plants in the bryophytes have spores that are homosporous in the morphological sense, but that are heterosporous in function. Some spores give rise to male gametophytes, whereas others give rise to female ones, and both types of spores develop in the same sporangium. Where tetrad analysis is possible (as in the liverwort *Sphaerocarpos donnellii,* in which the four haploid spores developed after meiosis remain united in a tetrad), it is found that the factors responsible for sex determination segregate at meiosis, with two spores of a tetrad giving rise to male plants and two giving rise to female ones. (Sex determination will be discussed in Chapter 5.) This condition is called *functional heterospory* and occurs in those morphologically homosporous plants that have dioecious gametophytes. Development of the gametophyte is exosporic, like those of homosporous plants in general. In the bryophytes only rarely is there a tendency toward morphological heterospory. When it does occur, as in some species of the moss *Macromitrium,* both types of spores develop in the same sporangium; sex is determined by genetic factors that segregate at meiosis.

With the background just provided, we will now turn to a consideration of the evolution of the seed. The earliest land plants were all homosporous, but heterosporous plants and plants bearing seeds and seedlike structures were well represented in the fossil record by the late Devonian and the early Carboniferous. In addition to members of the Spermopsida, seedlike structures also were formed both in some of the fossil lycopsids and pteropsids.

Major changes which occurred during the evolution of the seed were (1) change from homospory to heterospory with the concomitant change from exosporic to endosporic gametophytes; (2) reduction in the number of megaspores formed in the megasporangium, until only a single functional megaspore is formed; (3) retention of the female gametophyte within the unopened sporangium where fertilization and embryo development occur; and (4) envelopment of the sporangium by integumentary tissue. The integumentary tissue developed into the protective seed coat of the mature seed.

Reproduction in the heterosporous lycopsid *Selaginella* (see Figure 3·13) will be described in some detail because the genetic variation in this genus allows us to document several of the stages presumed to have occurred during seed evolution. The microgametophyte of *Selaginella* is retained within the microspore wall during most of its development, and the gametophyte at maturity consists of little more than a single antheridium (Figure 3·13B). Reduction of the male gametophyte to little more than an antheridium foreshadows its even more extreme reduction in the pollen grain of seed plants. The megagametophyte

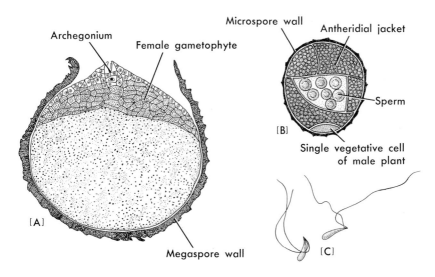

Figure 3·13. Gametophytes of *Selaginella*, a heterosporous lycopsid. A: Female gametophyte, with a single archegonium. **B:** Male gametophyte enclosed in microspore wall. **C:** Biflagellate sperm. [Redrawn from William H. Brown, *The Plant Kingdom*, Boston: Ginn and Company, 1935.]

likewise is retained within the megaspore wall until late in development, at which time the spore coat ruptures. The exposed part of the mega-gametophyte usually develops chlorophyll and archegonia develop within this exposed pad of tissue (Figure 3·13A).

Seed plants typically have only a single megagametophyte in each megasporangium. A decrease in the number of functional megaspores per sporangium must have occurred. In *Selaginella* most of the large number of spore mother cells in the megasporangium degenerate prior to meiosis; from one to ten survive. In most species only a single spore mother cell survives and undergoes meiosis. The fate of the four haploid daughter cells varies in the different species. In some, all develop into megaspores, whereas, at the other extreme, only a single megaspore matures in other species. A similar event occurred in *Lepidocarpon*, a genus of fossil lycopsids from the Carboniferous. Here only a single functional megaspore was formed, the other three haploid cells result-ing from meiosis aborted. Furthermore, the functional megaspore and the female gametophyte were retained within the megasporangium, which, in turn, was enveloped by modified leaf tissue. The general structure of *Lepidocarpon* is quite seedlike, and it probably functioned like a seed. However, it probably should not be called a seed because the mature sporangium dehisced. (The mature sporangium of the Spermopsida does not dehisce.) In a few extant species of *Selaginella* the megaspores are occasionally not discharged from the opened sporangium and fertilization and embryo development occur within the megasporangium. The occasional retention of the megaspore in the sporangium of *Selaginella* is significant in that it foreshadows the con-sistent retention of the megaspore within the megasporangium in plants like *Lepidocarpon* and in the ovule of seed plants.

In the preceding paragraphs a general description was given of the steps that probably occurred during the evolution of the seed. It should be noted that there is no evidence to suggest that *Selaginella*, or any other lycopsid, or any extant higher cryptogam has a close phylogenetic relationship to the seed plants (gymnosperms and angiosperms). *Sela-ginella* was used as an example because reproductive variability in this genus documents how the seed might have evolved. The seeds of the Spermopsida evolved independently of the seedlike structures of *Lepidocarpon* and of the other fossil higher cryptogams. However, it is probable that all seeds evolved along the general lines described.

Diversity

THE HIGHER cryptogams have essentially the same life cycle and they have many features in common. The variations in form and structure to be described in this chapter are to be considered as variations of a basic plan. Each Class of higher cryptogams (with the possible exception of the hornworts, fossils of which have not yet been found in the older geologic record) has been a separate phylogenetic line distinct at least by the beginning of the Carboniferous and probably prior to the early Devonian. This is ample time for the development of a considerable amount of diversity.

The purpose of this chapter is to describe the major characteristics of each higher cryptogam group and to point out some of the diversity within each group. About 34,500 species of higher cryptogams have been described. (There are about 6,500 species of green algae and over 300,000 species of seed plants.) Much of the diversity will be given only superficial treatment because of the small size of this book.

Hornworts

The hornworts, or anthocerotes, are a small, well-defined group of five genera (*Anthoceros, Phaeoceros, Megaceros, Dendroceros,* and *Notothylas*). Except for the polar land masses, they occur worldwide, commonly on soil; a few are epiphytic. Hornworts are easily overlooked in the field and easily misidentified, because the gametophytes may be confused with liverworts or fern prothalli and the sporophytes with blades of grass.

The form of the dorsiventrally flattened gametophyte varies with the species, but the environment also will influence the phenotype. One

Figure 4·1. *Anthoceros fusiformis.* Growth habit of prostrate gametophyte and erect sporophyte.

type is shown in Figure 4·1. There is no tissue differentiation and little cell specialization in the gametophytic thallus. Thin sections of living plants of many species often strikingly reveal the presence of copious amounts of mucilage, which is contained in specialized mucilage cells in some species or in schizogenously formed intercellular cavities in others. The mucilage is a mixture and contains polysaccharides, but complete chemical characterization has not yet been made.

The lower surface of the thallus of many species contains stomalike pores that lead into cavities which are usually filled with slime (Figure 4·2A). Hormogones of blue-green algae (often species of *Nostoc*) move through these pores into the cavities where they multiply and form colonies. Those species of blue-green algae capable of nitrogen fixation presumably benefit their hornwort symbiont in much the same way that nitrogen-fixing bacteria are of benefit to their leguminous hosts. Use of axenic cultures of hornworts has shown that normal growth and development of the hornwort is not dependent on the presence of blue-green algae, either nitrogen-fixers or others. However, the importance of symbiotic nitrogen-fixers to the development of hornworts in the field is unknown.

The occurrence of the stomalike pores in the gametophytes of hornworts is of interest in that the pore originates in a manner comparable to the development of stoma between guard cells in the sporophytes of land plants. Unlike the stomatal apparatus, however, the two cells surrounding each pore in the gametophyte remain thin-walled and do not function to control pore size; the pore remains completely open. Moreover, the chambers are filled with slime and blue-green algae, making an aerating system nonfunctional. Perhaps the pore-chamber system can best be interpreted as a vestigial remnant of a previously extensive aerating system which functioned either in the early but now extinct hornworts or in the progenitors of the hornworts. This type of stomalike pore does not occur in gametophytes of other contemporary land plants, nor has the geologic record yielded much information about changes in form and structure of gametophytes during the evolution of land plants.

Only the hornworts among the land plants have chloroplasts with pyrenoids (Figure 4·2C), a character shared with the green algae. The pyrenoids of green algae and hornworts appear to function similarly in that starch granules are synthesized at the periphery of the pyrenoid in both groups. (We know almost nothing about how the pyrenoid is involved in carbohydrate metabolism in any plant group.) There is

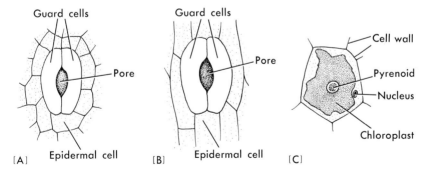

Figure 4·2. A, B: _Phaeoceros pearsoni._ A: Pore on lower surface of gametophyte thallus. **B:** Pore leading to substomatal chamber in sporophyte tissue. **C: _Notothylas orbicularis._** Cell of gametophyte showing a single chloroplast with a single pyrenoid.

variation, even within a single genus of hornworts (e.g., *Megaceros*), in the number of chloroplasts in each cell and in the presence or absence of pyrenoids. In what is probably the primitive condition, some hornworts (e.g., *Anthoceros*) have a single chloroplast with a single pyrenoid per cell. In several other species there is a tendency for the chloroplasts in the interior tissue of the thallus to be more numerous and to be smaller than those in the exterior tissue. In some species there may be as many as four to six chloroplasts per cell. Changes also occur in the distribution of the pyrenoid material within the chloroplasts. The chloroplasts in some species contain a single compact pyrenoid. In others, the pyrenoid occurs in two or three irregular pieces or as many tiny fragments within the chloroplast. Still other species have no pyrenoids. If the assumption is correct that land plants evolved from green algae, then one of the cellular modifications that occurred was the change from plants with one pyrenoid-containing chloroplast per cell to organisms with many apyrenoidal chloroplasts per cell. The type of variation in chloroplast number and structure in the hornworts can be used to indicate how the small, apyrenoidal chloroplasts of land plants might have evolved from large, pyrenoidal chloroplasts.

The gametangia of hornworts are embedded in gametophytic tissue. Although the cap cells of the archegonium neck are even with the thallus surface, the antheridium develops within a cavity and is exposed only upon rupture of the overlying tissue. It has been found that sex organ initiation is under environmental control. Experiments by Ridgway (1967) showed that antheridia are induced under short-day conditions (twelve hours or less of light diurnally) and that temperature has little effect. In these plants sex organs develop at that time of year (fall, winter, and spring) when water (needed for fertilization) is normally plentiful.

The mature sporophyte consists of a foot, embedded in the gametophytic thallus, and a terete spore-producing capsular region (Figure 4·1 and 4·3A). Prolonged growth in length of the sporophyte is possible through the continued activity of a meristematic region, an intercalary meristem, at the juncture of foot and capsule. Theoretically, the sporophyte should be capable of unlimited growth in length, but this is never realized in nature and sporophyte growth in culture has been equally limited. The oldest part of the capsule is at the apex because new cells are continually added to the base. Maturation of the capsule is from the apex downward. In many species the capsule ruptures along two preformed lines of weakness, which extend vertically the length of the capsule. The two valves thus formed twist upon drying and thereby aid in spore discharge by allowing the wind to blow away the exposed spores. The splitting of the capsule does not extend into the immature parts of the capsule, however. Cell division and differentiation occur for an extended time period, so that a large capsule discharges mature spores from the apical region while meiosis and spore development continue in the lower portion.

The sporophyte of hornworts reaches a greater degree of complexity and greater longevity than that of any other bryophyte. Except for the genus *Notothylas,* the spore-producing tissue represents but a small fraction of the total tissue. The capsule is jacketed by a highly differentiated photosynthetic tissue and each cell of this tissue generally contains a single chloroplast, although this is in need of further study. Stomata (Figure 4·2B) and substomatal chambers are present in two (*Anthoceros* and *Phaeoceros*) of the five genera. A slender columella

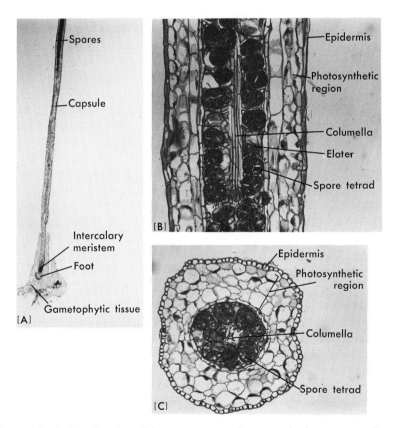

Figure 4·3. A: Longisection of hornwort sporophyte attached to gametophyte. Note intimate contact between foot of sporophyte and gametophyte and location of the intercalary meristem. **B: Longisection of sporophyte capsule in region of spore tetrads.** Note elaters interspersed with spore tetrads. **C: Cross section of capsule showing the cylinder of sporogenous tissue surrounding the columella.**

of elongate cells extends the length of the spore-producing region of the capsule. These cells are thin-walled in most species, but Proskauer (1960) found that the outermost layer of the columella in two species possesses helical secondary wall thickenings as do the elaters of these two species. The preceding paper by Proskauer presents a pertinent discussion of the phylogenetic implications of the occurrence of helically thickened columella cells in hornworts and an evaluation of the relationship of hornworts with other higher cryptogams.

The sporogenous tissue of anthocerotes forms a cylinder between the central columella and the photosynthetic jacket (Figure 4·3B,C). Two types of cells differentiate in this tissue—cells that undergo meiosis (see Chapter 2 for an account of hornwort spore mother cells) and cells that develop into elaters. The elaters remain thin-walled in some species, but in others the elaters possess a helical pattern of secondary wall thickening. A discussion of elater function is given in the next section.

Liverworts

The fossil record of liverworts extends back at least to the Carboniferous. Moreover, plant fragments possibly of a liverwort have been described from Devonian strata of North America (Hueber, 1966). Perhaps the most interesting feature of the Carboniferous and later fossil liverworts is their close similarity to the gametophytes of contemporary ones. Only one fossil liverwort, *Naiadita lanceolata,* described from the Triassic of England, differs markedly (see Harris, 1938). Few fossil liverwort sporophytes have been found, but those that have are similar to the sporophytes of contemporary liverworts. The geologic age and apparent morphological conservatism of liverworts are noteworthy.

Some 9,000 species of liverworts have been described. They are quite diverse in gametophyte form, structure, and physiological tolerances. Although liverworts thrive in a wide variety of habitats, their growth is most luxuriant in moist environments. Most grow on the ground or as epiphytes; only a few are (secondarily) aquatic. In consideration of their geologic age and the large number of species of living organisms, one must conclude that the liverworts are a very successful group in spite of their usually being an inconspicuous part of the flora.

The most definitive features of the liverworts come not from the gametophyte, as one might expect, but from the relatively short-lived sporophyte. The mature sporophyte consists of a foot (embedded in gametophytic tissue), seta, and capsule (Figure 4·5A). (The absence of a seta and foot in *Riccia* is presumably a derived condition.) The

Growing point

Midrib

[A]

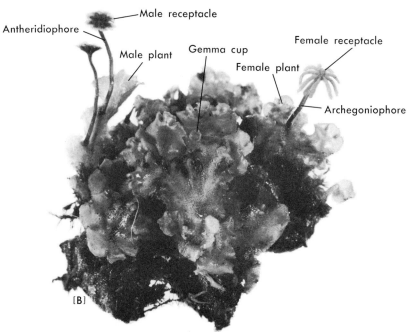

Male receptacle

Antheridiophore

Male plant

Gemma cup

Female receptacle

Female plant

Archegoniophore

[B]

Figure 4·4. A: *Riccia.* **Habit of growth on soil.** Gametangia develop in midrib tissue. **B:** *Marchantia polymorpha,* **a dioecious liverwort.** Archegoniophores and antheridiophores elevate the gametangia above the thallus surface.

67

sporophyte capsule usually contains elaters or other nonspore cells in addition to spores. The liverwort sporophyte is formed by over-all cell division and differentiation; there is no region of localized meristematic activity. (Compare with the activity of the intercalary meristem in hornworts.) The pattern of sporophyte growth and differentiation together with the absence of stomata and of a columella (two consistent negative characteristics) serve to separate the liverworts as a group from the other higher cryptogams.

For convenience the liverworts may be separated into two groups based on the form of the spore mother cell. One group (composed of the orders Marchantiales and Sphaerocarpales) has spore mother cells that prior to meiosis are typically spherical in outline. The spore mother cells in the other group (including the orders Jungermanniales and Calobryales) become four-lobed.

The order Marchantiales is the larger group of liverworts that have spherical spore mother cells. Characteristically, these are thalloid liverworts usually with a definite midrib (Figure 4·4) and the thallus often has considerable complexity. Numerous pores occur on the upper surface of the thallus of most species. These pores are analogous to stomata in that they provide an avenue for gas exchange between the internal tissue and the external atmosphere, but the pores develop in a different manner. Moreover, the cells that border the pores do not regulate pore size, as do the guard cells surrounding stomata. The pores open into fingerlike depressions (in some species of *Riccia*) or into larger internal chambers (as in *Marchantia*) (Figure 4·5B,C). Highly chlorophyllose filaments (chlorenchyma) may be present in the chambers; but when these are absent the bulk of photosynthesis occurs in the richly chlorophyllose cells that line the chambers. The underlying tissue lacks air spaces, generally has few chloroplasts, and usually contains abundant food reserve. In many of the Marchantiales an endophytic fungus is a normal symbiont in the storage tissue. The type of symbiotic relationship present (e.g., mutualism or parasitism) remains to be determined.

Unicellular rhizoids and two rows of multicellular scales occur on the lower surface of the thallus. The young scales overarch the apex, protecting the meristematic cells at the growing point. Vertically oriented rhizoids serve to anchor the plant to the substrate. In many species a second set of rhizoids with pegs of wall material (called peg rhizoids) extends horizontally along the midrib being held in place by the scales (Figure 4·5C). These rhizoids aid in the horizontal conduction of water and dissolved minerals along the midrib.

Both monoecious and dioecious species occur. In plants such as *Riccia* (Figure 4·4A) the archegonia and antheridia are embedded in the midrib. In others the gametangia are clustered in specialized re-

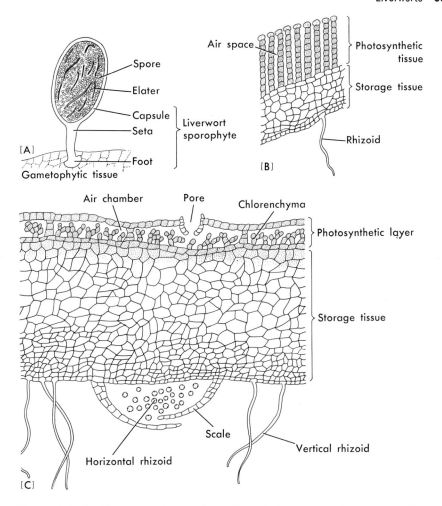

Figure 4·5. A: Diagrammatic representation of the form and structure of a liverwort sporophyte. B: *Riccia*. Cross section of a portion of the thallus. Note photosynthetic filaments and underlying storage tissue. **C: *Marchantia polymorpha*.** Cross section of thallus segment in midrib region. Note thallus differentiation.

ceptacles that may or may not be elevated above the thallus surface. The antheridia and archegonia of *Marchantia* (Figure 4·4B) are borne on elevated structures called *antheridiophores* and *archegonio-phores,* respectively. The elevated structures represent highly modified thallus branches. Their morphological nature is demonstrated by the occurrence of rhizoids that extend the length of the gametangiophores and by the presence of air chambers in the expanded cap of the gametangiophores.

In the Marchantiales the antheridia develop in chambers sunk in the dorsal surface of the thallus or of the antheridiophore. A canal through which sperm pass during antheridial discharge provides access to the external environment. In *Marchantia* the slightly raised edge of the cap of the antheridiophore enables rain water to collect and the sperm are discharged into this water. Sperm dissemination then occurs by the splashing of raindrops on the receptacle. However, most Marchantialean liverworts exhibit an explosive discharge of sperm from the antheridium. The sperm are shot above the thallus in a visible puff, and wind and water currents then aid in sperm dissemination.

On the archegoniophore the archegonium is borne on the lower surface, with the neck pointing downward. Fertilization generally occurs prior to the elevation of the archegonium above the surface of the thallus, at which time the neck of the archegonium is close to the substrate. This is important because water is necessary for movement of the sperm to the archegonium, and the chances for fertilization are increased when the archegonial neck is immersed in a film of water close to the substrate. The sporophyte also remains suspended from the archegoniophore, and at maturity the capsule is lowered beyond the enveloping gametophytic tissue by elongation of the cells of the seta. Elaters with helical bands of secondary wall material are present in the capsule of most of these liverworts. Elaters function to discharge spores from the dehisced capsule; their twisting and jerking movements are in response to drying.

In *Riccia,* as mentioned earlier, the archegonium is embedded in midrib tissue, with its neck protruding above the thallus surface. The sporophyte consists of a capsule only; there is no seta or foot and even the capsule wall disappears before the spores mature. The mature spores remain embedded in midrib tissue of the gametophyte and are liberated on the death and decay of the parent plant. Elaters are absent from the capsule.

Members of the order Sphaerocarpales also have spherical spore mother cells. The gametophytes of the three genera (*Riella, Sphaerocarpos,* and *Geothallus*) are simpler in form and structure than are those of the Marchantiales. The plant consists of a midrib bearing a unistratose wing (*Riella*) or bearing two rows of leaflike structures (*Geothallus* and *Sphaerocarpos*). In *Sphaerocarpos* archegonia and antheridia occur scattered along the midrib and are enveloped individually in flask-shaped structures (bottles) (Figure 5·8). The form of the sporophyte is similar to that of the other liverworts. However, the seta does not elongate at sporophyte maturity. The sporogenous tissue differentiates into two kinds of cells, one kind that becomes spore mother cells and undergoes meiosis and one kind that develops chloroplasts, stores a large amount of starch, and does not undergo meiosis (Figure 2·7). The starch gradually disappears during spore development and these nonmeiotic cells presumably have a nutritive function. Elaters do not occur in the Sphaerocarpales.

The order Jungermanniales, with both thalloid and leafy representatives, is the largest group of liverworts. (The Calobryales, also with four-lobed spore mother cells, will not be discussed.) Many of the Jungermanniales, like *Porella* and *Frullania*, are differentiated into stemlike and leaflike structures (Figure 4·6A,B). These are the leafy liverworts. Most of them are dorsiventrally flattened with two rows of lateral leaves (lateral photosynthetic organs) borne on a stemlike axis. A third row of leaves, called underleaves (or amphigastria), may or may not be present on the lower surface of the axis. The leafy liverwort *Herberta* is difficult to distinguish from a moss because it has radial

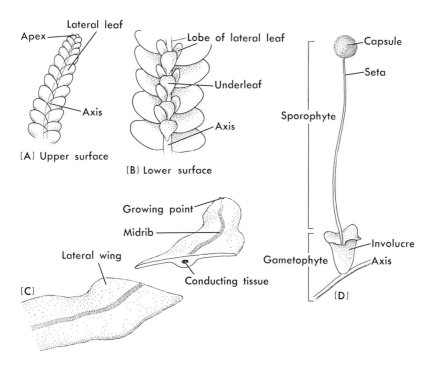

Figure 4·6. Jungermanniales. A, B: *Porella*. A: Upper surface of plant. Two rows of lateral leaves are evident. **B:** Lower surface of plant. A third row of leaves, underleaves, are also present in this liverwort. **C: *Pallavicinia*.** General form of thallus and thallus cross section showing position of conducting strand. **D: Sporophyte of *Fossombronia longiseta*.** Leaves of the gametophyte have not been drawn. The slender, colorless seta elevates the globose capsule above the thallus surface.

symmetry with three ranks of helically inserted leaves, and the leaves are of equal size. The thalloid Jungermannialean plants, like the commonly studied *Pellia,* have a thickened midrib bearing lateral, usually unistratose, wings (Figures 4·6C; 2·9E).

Neither the thalloid nor the leafy Jungermannialean liverworts have the degree of internal complexity of the Marchantiales. An air chamber system does not occur. The leaves or lateral wings and the outer layers of the midrib serve as the main photosynthetic tissues. Typically, there is little tissue or cell specialization in the midrib. An exception is the occurrence of elongate cells specialized for water conduction in a few thalloid plants such as *Pallavicinia* (Figure 4·6C) and *Symphyogyna.* These cells structurally and functionally resemble the water-conducting cells of vascular plants. Smith (1966) reported the existence of complete perforations between adjacent water-conducting elements in *Symphyogyna,* a condition similar to that found in vessel elements of vascular plants. However, the occurrence of these cells is restricted to the gametophyte in liverworts and there is no evidence that the cells are lignified.

Sexual reproduction in the Jungermanniales is essentially similar to that described in the Marchantiales, except that gametangiophores are never formed. In the leafy liverwort *Porella* gametangia of both sexes are borne on short lateral branches; the antheridia develop in leaf axils and the archegonia develop at the apices of separate branches. The archegonia of *Porella,* and of many other leafy liverworts, are surrounded by a *perianth,* which is composed of modified leaves. In the thalloid *Pellia* archegonia develop in clusters at the apex of the main branch and are covered by a unistratose flap of tissue called an *involucre.* The antheridia of this plant are scattered on the dorsal surface of the thallus and are covered by a layer of cells. The antheridia and archegonia of *Fossombronia* develop scattered along the midrib of the plant and are not protected by specialized tissues. In *Fossombronia longiseta* the two kinds of sex organs occasionally occur intermixed on the thallus, but generally a period of antheridial formation alternates with a period of archegonial formation in this monoecious plant.

The sporophyte (like the sporophyte of liverworts in general) is differentiated into foot, seta, and capsule. However, the capsule (containing elaters in addition to spores) is usually more massive and the seta undergoes more extensive elongation than in the Marchantiales (Figure 4·6D). There is no cell division during seta elongation, the increase in height being entirely due to enlargement in the vertical direction of pre-existing cells. An elongate seta places the capsule in a position favorable for wind dispersal of spores upon capsule dehiscence.

Vegetative reproduction is very common in the liverworts, and some, especially in the Arctic region, reproduce solely by this means. The formation of gemmae occurs in the Marchantiales (*Marchantia* and *Lunularia*, for example) and in the Jungermanniales (*Blasia* and *Calypogeia,* among others) (see Figures 2·9 and 4·4). Tuber formation occurs in several liverworts and is particularly widespread in the genus *Fossombronia.*

Mosses

The fossil record of mosses like that of liverworts extends back into the Paleozoic. The earliest record of a moss, although only a fragment of a plant, comes from the Upper Carboniferous of France. Several beautifully preserved mosses have also been described from Upper and Lower Permian strata of Russia. Only gametophytes have been found so far and, like those of the liverworts, they are "modern" in general aspect. One problematic moss, *Sporogonites exuberans,* has been described from the Lower Devonian of Europe (Andrews, 1960). This plant possessed an oval sporangium borne at the apex of a slender, unbranched stalk at least 4 cm long. A dome-shaped mass of spores, similar to that in *Sphagnum,* occurred in the sporangium. Unfortunately, the organic material at the base of the stalk is extremely poorly preserved. *Sporogonites* might in fact quite likely be a moss. However, only the discovery of more completely preserved specimens will enable us to determine the affinities of this fossil with more certainty.

Like the liverworts, the contemporary mosses are worldwide in distribution and have their most luxuriant development in wet and humid regions. Individual species are generally more restricted in distribution. Some can be used as indicator organisms in that they characteristically occur on specific substrates or in specific environments. Some mosses can tolerate such bizarre substrates as the dung of caribou and other mammals in the Arctic region (e.g., *Splachnum*) or heavy metal deposits (e.g., *Mercyia*). Mosses that normally occur on, and in nature are often restricted to, bizarre habitats have been shown to grow well in the laboratory on simple inorganic media. In contrast to other mosses, these mosses are capable of utilizing or at least tolerating these substrates. As yet the nutritional and environmental tolerances of mosses, and of other higher cryptogams, have been little explored.

The ability to withstand periodic desiccation is a characteristic of many mosses, especially those of the temperate and more arid climates. In these regions dried mosses that quickly revive upon wetting are familiar sights, especially on stone buildings, barns, fence posts, rocks, and tree trunks. Physiological drought also occurs in those mosses that are able to survive being frozen in ice and snow during the winter.

During freezing, ice crystal formation begins first in the environment external to the plant tissue. Intracellular water then moves rapidly out through the cell membrane and cell wall, and this water is added to the growing ice crystals external to the plant. The relative ease with which the cells of these mosses lose water protects the plant against intracellular ice crystal formation and consequent damage to the cellular membranes. Plants completely frozen in ice contain only water that is tightly bound chemically. In effect, the plants are dehydrated. These mosses readily resume vegetative growth when they are chipped out of the ice and brought into a warm laboratory.

Upon casual glance mosses generally look alike. Closer scrutiny reveals considerable variation in form and structure. In fact, mosses are the largest group of higher cryptogams, with over 14,000 described species. The basic moss life cycle, like that of the other higher cryptogams, consists of two multicellular growth phases: a leafy, gamete-producing growth phase and a nonleafy, spore-producing one (Figure 4·7). Evolution has occurred in both growth phases, but little of the variation will be explored here.

The mature gametophyte is the conspicuous and long-lived form of the moss plant. This consists of a main axis bearing leaves and is anchored by multicellular rhizoids. Some aspects of moss anatomy have been discussed in Chapter 3 (see also Hébant, 1964 and 1967, for information on the conducting tissues of bryophytes in general). Anatomically, the stem of most mosses consists of an epidermis, a cortex, and a central column of elongate cells (Figure 4·8). The most complex cell and tissue differentiation occurs in *Polytrichum,* where steroids (thick-walled supportive cells), leptoids (food-conducting cells), and hydroids (water-conducting cells) all occur in the central region of the stem. A layer of parenchymatous cells containing starch (the starch sheath) delimits the cortex from the central region.

Water conduction in moss gametophytes has been the subject of several studies. Experiments have shown that in mosses with relatively thick cuticles, such as in *Polytrichum,* water conduction generally occurs in the hydroids of the stem. On the other hand, external water conduction is common in mosses with thin cuticles. Here water moves up the plant by surface tension and is rapidly absorbed through the leaf cells. Internal water conduction plays only a minor role in the water economy of these plants. Both internal and external water conduction have been shown to occur in still other mosses.

The leaves are the main photosynthetic organs of the adult moss plant. In most cases the three ranks of leaves are helically inserted and the plants have radial symmetry. In *Neckera* the leaves are flattened into one plane and the flattened appearance of *Fissidens* is due to the

Figure 4·7. *Polytrichum juniperinum*. The leafless sporophyte is attached to the leafy gametophyte. The calyptra has been removed from the left sporophyte.

formation of two ranks of leaves only. The leaves of mosses are mostly one cell in thickness except for a thickened midrib (also called a nerve or costa). A more highly differentiated leaf occurs in *Polytrichum*. In this genus a series of parallel longitudinal lamellae or plates of cells extend most of the length of the upper surface of the leaf (Figure 4·9). The cells of the unistratose lamellae contain numerous chloroplasts. Upon drying, the leaf margins curl in slightly and the leaves become appressed to the stem and thereby protect the thin-walled photosynthetic tissue from too rapid desiccation. Generally, the midrib of the leaf does not extend into the stem cortex, but when it does (e.g., in *Mnium*, Figure 4·8), the leaf trace rarely connects to the central cylinder. In *Mnium* unspecialized parenchyma cells occur between the base of the leaf trace and the central cylinder of the stem. On the other hand, the leaf trace of *Polytrichum* does extend across the cortex to form a loose connection with the central cylinder.

The capacity for vegetative reproduction is widespread in the mosses.

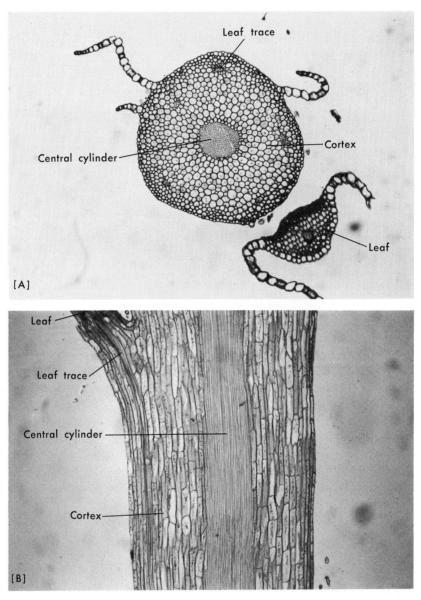

Figure 4·8. *Mnium*. A: Stem cross section showing the central cylinder of hydroids and leaf trace in cortex. **B:** Stem longisection showing thin, elongate hydroids of the central cylinder. Note extension of the leaf trace into the cortex.

Almost any part of the gametophyte—leaf, stem, or rhizoid—is capable of regenerating a new gametophyte. Moss regeneration takes a somewhat different course from that which takes place in animals. In animals, regeneration leads to the formation of the missing part, whereas regeneration in mosses leads to the development of a whole new adult gametophyte. Normally, moss regeneration leads first to the development of a protonema, the juvenile growth phase (see later), and then to the development of the adult plant; the developmental cycle of the gametophyte is repeated. The direct development of the mature gametophyte is possible under certain experimental conditions, but even here an entirely new plant develops, not just the missing plant part. A few mosses, such as *Aulacomnium* (Figure 2·9) and *Tetraphis,* also reproduce vegetatively by means of multicellular gemmae and others may reproduce by the formation of stoloniferous branches.

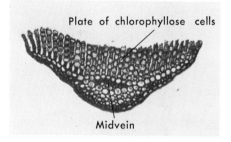

Figure 4·9. *Polytrichum*. Leaf cross section. Numerous plates of chlorophyllose cells extend the length of the upper (adaxial) surface of the leaf.

Plate of chlorophyllose cells

Midvein

The mature gametophyte is appropriately called a *gametophore* because it bears the gametangia. The gametangia develop at the apex either of the main gametophore axis or of short lateral branches. The spatial relationship of the male and female gametangia to each other is variable, depending on the species. In some, both gametangial types develop together at the apex of the same gametophore; in others, the gametangia develop on separate branches of the same plant; and in still other mosses, the antheridia and archegonia develop on separate plants. Except for a very long neck on the archegonium, the male and female gametangia of mosses closely resemble those of liverworts. In mosses, antheridia and archegonia are interspersed among numerous filaments called *paraphyses* (Figure 4·10). The function of paraphyses is unknown; it has been suggested that they might function to protect the gametangia from drying out by increasing the surface area on which capillary water may be held. Like the highter cryptogams in general, water is needed for fertilization.

The zygote begins development almost immediately following fertilization. During the early growth of the sporophyte, mitotic divisions

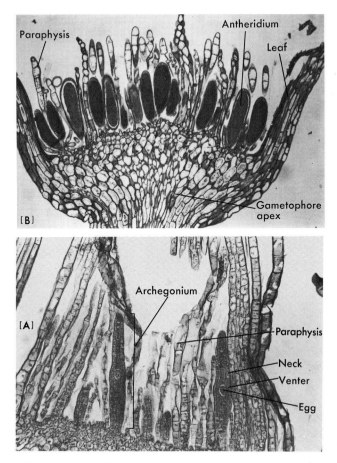

Figure 4·10. *Mnium*. A: Gametophore apex bearing immature archegonia interspersed with paraphyses. **B:** Gametophore apex bearing antheridia interspersed with paraphyses.

also occur in the venter of the archegonium. For a time cell division and cell enlargement of this archegonial tissue keep pace with the growth of the enclosed sporophyte. However, continued enlargement of the sporophyte finally ruptures the archegonium and the upper part of the archegonium is carried aloft as a covering, the *calyptra,* over the apex of the sporophyte. The form of the calyptra is useful in the identification of some mosses. The calyptra of *Polytrichum* is shown in Figure 4·7. Experiments have shown that the calyptra is necessary for the normal development of the sporophyte. Premature removal of the calyptra results in precocious swelling of the apex of the sporophyte.

The young sporophyte is spindle-shaped and has a region of meristematic activity at each apex. The basal end of the embryonic sporophyte grows down through the base of the archegonium and penetrates the underlying gametophytic tissue. This part of the sporophyte, the foot, securely anchors the sporophyte to the gametophyte. It also serves as the pathway by which water and dissolved substances pass from the gametophyte into the growing sporophyte. The other end of the sporophyte grows upward and gives rise to the seta and the capsule (Figure 4·7).

The seta characteristically elevates the capsule, containing the sporangium, above the level of the gametophyte. Anatomically, the leafless seta is stemlike. An epidermis with a cuticle forms the outermost layer. The cortical cells that immediately underlie the epidermis are thick-walled and have a supportive function. The cortex surrounds a central strand containing thin-walled hydroids (Figure 4·11A). Moreover leptoids have also been found in the setae of some mosses. Leptoid function during sporophyte growth and development needs investigation.

The capsule is a complex organ and is differentiated into three general regions, each with a distinctive function. The basal region, the part that is confluent with the seta, is called the *apophysis* and is specialized for photosynthesis. Abundant chlorenchyma and the stomata, when present, occur in this part of the capsule.

The sporangium occurs in the central part of the capsule. In *Polytrichum* the sporangium occurs as a cylinder around a central pillar of nonsporogenous tissue, called the *columella* (Figure 4·11B–D). Large air sacs separate the sporangium from the columella on the one side and from the capsule wall on the other. Filaments of cells that traverse the air sacs hold the sporangium in position. The sporogenous tissue of the sporangium, which is unistratose in the young capsule, enlarges greatly during later development (Figure 4·11C,D). Unlike liverworts and hornworts, all cells of the sporogenous tissue undergo meiosis and give rise to tetrads of spores. No sterile cells such as elaters are present in any species of moss. In mosses like *Polytrichum* the interior cells except for the spores degenerate at capsule maturity, so that the spores come to lie free in an otherwise hollow capsule. At this time the spores are ready for discharge.

The apical portion of the moss capsule is specialized to regulate spore discharge. A lid, or *operculum,* occurs at the capsule apex and becomes visible when the calyptra falls off (Figure 4·7, 4·12A). In turn, the operculum drops off when the mature capsule begins to dry. Many mosses have one or more whorls of *peristome teeth* that lie immediately under the operculum and become exposed when the operculum falls away. The form, number, structure, and size of the teeth and associated structures at the apical end of the capsule are variable

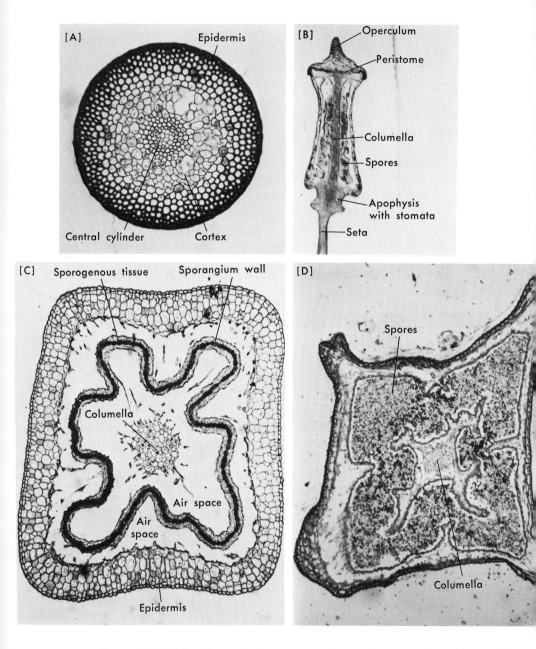

Figure 4·11. Polytrichum. A: Cross section of sporophyte seta. Note the central strand of thin-walled hydroids. **B:** Longisection of a nearly mature capsule. **C:** Cross section of a young capsule. Note the darkly stained sporogenous tissue surrounded by a unistratose sporangium wall. **D:** Cross section of a nearly mature capsule.

and these details are widely used in moss identification. The peristome teeth of four mosses are shown in Figure 4·12. Presence of teeth at the capsule apex slows the rate of spore discharge. Moreover, the teeth of many mosses respond to changes in humidity in such a way that openings between adjacent teeth develop with a lowering of humidity. For example, in *Funaria* (Figure 4·12C) the peristome teeth are united at their tips, and slight rotation of the teeth as a result of changes in humidity allows spores to filter out through slits between adjacent teeth. The filiform, helically twisted teeth of *Tortula* (Figure 4·12D) also show slight hygroscopic movement and the spores slowly filter out of the capsule. The teeth of *Polytrichum* (Figure 4·12B) and of its relative *Atrichum* (Figure 4·12E) are incapable of movement. Here spore discharge is regulated by the up and down movements of the *epiphragm,* a drumheadlike covering over the capsule apex.

Although delayed spore discharge would seem to have distinct adaptive advantages for the moss, it should be pointed out that several mosses that lack any such regulatory device at the capsule apex are as widely distributed as are those that have them. Because there is evidence that these mosses which lack peristome teeth were reduced from mosses with teeth, the assumption is reasonable that the presence of teeth had a greater selective value for the moss in times gone by than at present.

Moss spores usually germinate rapidly when placed on a suitable substrate (see section on spore germination, Chapter 5). In *Sphagnum* a unistratose plate of cells, called a prothallus, soon develops and represents the juvenile growth phase of the gametophyte. However, in most mosses the juvenile growth phase is represented by an extensive and highly branched filamentous system, called the *protonema (proto,* "first"; *nema,* "a thread") (Figures 4·13; 5·4). The protonema resembles a highly branched green alga. Under favorable conditions the protonema is long-lived (it is perennial in laboratory culture) and can survive at lower light intensities than does the adult leafy plant. Extensive, green, feltlike protonemal mats are common along damp shaded paths and along stream banks.

The protonema of many mosses has two distinct growth phases, called the *chloronema* and the *caulonema.* In these mosses early protonemal growth following spore germination (or regeneration) consists of highly branched, richly chlorophyllose filaments that are anchored to the substrate by multicellular rhizoids. This is the chloronema and is further characterized by the presence of cells with transverse end walls, colorless cell walls, and many discoid chloroplasts. Continued growth of the protonema results in the development of the caulonema growth phase. The caulonema is differentiated into (1) multicellular

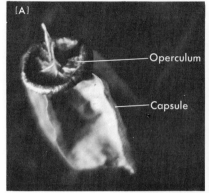

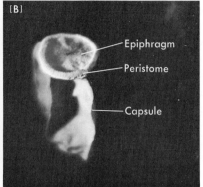

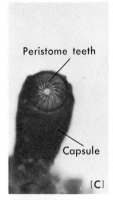

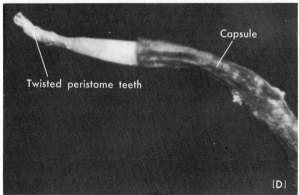

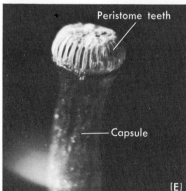

Figure 4·12. Moss peristomes. A, B: *Polytrichum*. A: The operculum covers the peristome. B: The operculum has been removed, exposing the teeth. Upon drying, the epiphragm moves upward and permits the spores to sift out between the teeth. C: *Funaria hygrometrica*. The sixteen peristome teeth, united at their tips, rotate in response to changes in humidity. D: *Tortula*. The filiform teeth exhibit slight hygroscopic movement. E: *Atrichum*. The spaces between the teeth are clearly evident in this relative of *Polytrichum*.

rhizoids, (2) prostrate, axial filaments, and (3) highly branched, aerial filaments (Figure 4·13). Cells of the aerial filaments are specialized for photosynthetic function and in general characteristics resemble cells of the chloronema. Cells of the prostrate, axial filaments are elongate and have rather thick, brownish walls. They also have oblique end walls and contain spindle-shaped chloroplasts. A cross section of an axial cell is shown in Figure 4·14. Overlapping end walls provide for greater surface area of contact between adjacent cells, and

Figure 4·13. *Funaria hygrometrica.* **A:** A young gametophore developed from the caulonema. The protonema is differentiated into axial and aerial filaments and rhizoids. **B:** An older gametophore, still attached to the protonema.

the end walls contain numerous plasmodesmata. The axial filaments appear to be specialized for the rapid conduction of dissolved materials. As indicated earlier, caulonema differentiation of the protonema is characteristic of many mosses, including *Funaria, Physcomitrium,* and *Tortula.* This differentiation does not occur in *Polytrichum,* however; only rhizoids and chloronemalike cells occur.

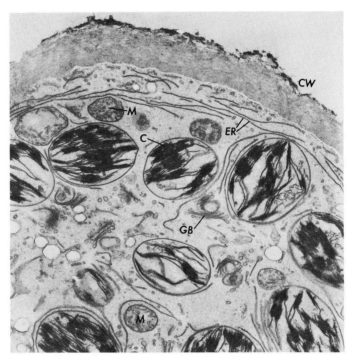

Figure 4·14. Electron microscope photo of a portion of a protonemal cell of *Tetraphis.* Note the large numbers of mitochondria (M) and Golgi bodies (GB), the grana differentiation in chloroplasts (C), the thick, fibrillar cell wall (CW), and the alignment of the endoplasmic reticulum (ER) parallel to the cell surface. (Fixation with potassium permanganate.) [Photo courtesy of Stewart Beaubien.]

The adult gametophyte, the gametophore, arises as a lateral outgrowth from the protonema (Figure 4·13). (The gametophore of *Sphagnum* arises as a lateral outgrowth from the margin of the flat prothallus.) The gametophore develops from a cell, the gametophore initial, which is one cell removed from an axial cell of the caulonema. This cell enlarges and the planes of cell division are oriented in such a way that an apical cell with three cutting faces is developed. Mitotic activity of the apical cell leads to the development of a small gametophore bud. Leaf primordia are soon formed and subsequent growth and differentiation of the bud results in the development of the adult moss plant.

Usually, many gametophores develop from a single protonema. The cells at the apices of the filaments continue to divide and enlarge as long as environmental conditions are favorable for growth and the gametophores continue to be initiated with time. The more recently initiated gametophores develop toward the periphery of the protonemal mat. (Factors that influence gametophore initiation are discussed in Chapter 5.) Continued gametophore initiation and development results in the formation of the compact cushions characteristic of many mosses seen in the field.

Psilopsids

A diverse vascular plant flora was in existence by the end of the Lower Devonian. Many of these plants had relatively simple organization and small size, generally from 10 to 90 cm in height (for example, the species of *Rhynia* shown in Figure 3·6 was about 20 cm in height). Plants classified as psilopsids have the following characteristics: (1) they lack roots; (2) they have leafless stems or scalelike lateral appendages; and (3) their sporangia are typically terminal, but are lateral in some. Two orders are conventionally recognized within the Psilopsida, the fossil forms are placed in the Psilophytineae (or Psilophytopsida) and contemporary ones in the Psilotineae (or Psilotopsida).

Two genera, *Psilotum* and *Tmesipteris,* are conventionally classified as Psilotineae. *Tmesipteris,* with perhaps a single species, occurs on the ground and as an epiphyte in the warm regions of Australasia and a few of the Pacific islands, including the Philippine Islands. Roots are absent. Definite leaflike lateral appendages, each with a single unbranched midvein, do occur, but their phylogenetic origin is still uncertain. Some students of plant morphology (e.g., Bold, 1967) have suggested that the appendages represent flattened lateral branches, whereas others have suggested an enation origin for these structures. In *Tmesipteris* two partially fused sporangia are borne on the adaxial surface near the base of some of these leaflike appendages.

Psilotum (Figure 4·15) has widespread distribution in subtropical and tropical regions; in the United States it has been found in Florida, Louisiana, Texas, and Arizona. An underground rhizome, anchored by unicellular rhizoids, gives rise to erect stems that dichotomize in three dimensions. The stem is the main photosynthetic organ, although small, green, scalelike appendages that lack a vascular strand are present. This rather simple-appearing vascular plant has a relatively simple stem

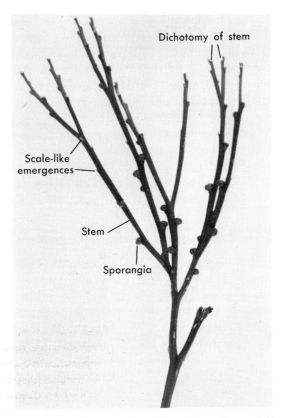

Dichotomy of stem

Scale-like
emergences

Stem

Sporangia

Figure 4·15. *Psilotum nudum,* **portion of a plant.** The scalelike emergences, sporangia, and dichotomous pattern of branching are evident.

anatomy (Figure 4·16). The central protostele is surrounded by a broad cortex. The spongy photosynthetic tissue of the stem is located immediately under the epidermis and numerous stomata permit gas exchange. The angular stem provides for increased photosynthetic area as well as greater mechanical rigidity of the stem.

The sporangial apparatus of *Psilotum* consists of three fused sporangia borne on a short stalk and subtended by a bifid scalelike appendage. Monoecious gametophytes develop from spores of this homosporous plant (Figure 4·16B). The nongreen, long-lived gametophytes are subterranean and contain an endophytic fungus as a normal symbiont. The multiflagellate sperm are released from the antheridia when sufficient soil water is available and fertilization occurs in the archegonium. Sperm chemotaxis has not been studied in either *Psilotum* or *Tmesipteris.*

The concept of the Psilophytineae is undergoing change. Renewed interest in the Paleozoic floras has led to the reworking of known Devonian fossil localities and the discovery of new ones. In turn, new taxa have been described and older ones have become known in greater, and more accurate, detail. It has now become apparent that the Psilophytineae most likely include at least two separate plant groups of simple organization that existed in the Devonian (cf. Banks, 1968; Boreau, 1967). Because continued research on the Devonian and Silurian floras probably will allow us to modify our concepts further in the future, it seems convenient to continue to use the category Psilophytineae here.

Rhynia is perhaps the most celebrated of the fossil psilopsids. Starting with the simple form of this plant, it is possible to visualize conceptu-

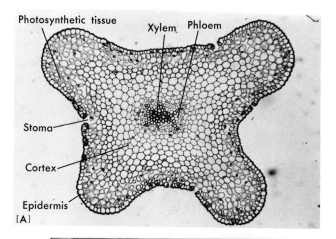

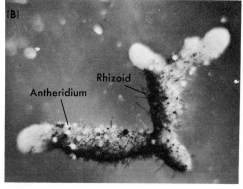

Figure 4·16. *Psilotum nudum.* **A:** Stem cross section. The photosynthetic tissue and an extensive air space system occur in the outer cortex of the stem. **B:** Gametophyte. The heterotrophic gametophyte leads a subterranean existence. (**B:** Photo courtesy of Dr. D. W. Bierhorst.)

ally how the more complex body of vascular plants could have evolved (see Chapter 3). A genus with two described species, *Rhynia* consists of an underground rhizome, anchored by unicellular rhizoids, and erect dichotomizing branches (Figure 3·7). Roots and leaves are absent. Excellent preservation in siliceous rock has made possible detailed anatomical investigations. The stem is protostelic, with tracheids but no vessel elements. The phloem is not well differentiated. A broad cortex surrounds the stele. Stomata in the epidermis of the aerial branches provide a means for gas exchange between the (presumably) photosynthetic tissue of the outer cortex and the external environment. The sporangia were borne singly at the apex of some of the branches and contain well-preserved spores. Spores in some of the sporangia are still in tetrads (in *Rhynia* as well as in some of the other fossil psilopsids) and therefore these are assumed to have been diploid plants. The nature of the haploid gametophyte, in all of the fossil psilopsids, remains unknown.

We now know that a remarkably large assemblage of plants with diverse morphology occurs in the fossil record earlier than and contemporaneously with *Rhynia*. That *Rhynia* was the primitive land plant from which other vascular plants evolved is unlikely. *Rhynia* should be considered a simple, but not primitive plant that coexisted with more complex ones during the Upper Devonian.

Many botanists have found the discontinuous fossil record of the psilopsids to be puzzling. Except for the two contemporary genera there is no evidence to indicate that psilopsids survived beyond the Devonian. The question has been raised whether *Psilotum* and *Tmesipteris* are simple plants because they have retained primitive features or whether they are simple because of evolutionary reduction. Are they reduced lycopsids rather than psilopsids? Continued study of the fossils in the geologic record and of the developmental potentialities of these two genera in the laboratory should help in solving this enigma.

Lycopsids

Vascular plants of unmistakable lycopsid (class Lycopsida) affinities have been found in Lower Devonian strata contemporaneous with the oldest known psilopsids. The strata that contains *Baragwanathia,* a lycopsidlike plant from Australia earlier thought to be of Upper Silurian age, has recently been reassigned to the Lower Devonian. The lycopsids flourished in the Upper Devonian and Carboniferous, but diminished in numbers during the Permian Period. Arborescent forms (*Lepidodendron* was over 30 m in height) were conspicuous and often dominant components of the coal swamp forests; herbaceous lycopsids were also present. Today, only five genera of lycopsids, all herbaceous, survive: *Lycopodium, Selaginella, Stylites, Isoetes,* and *Phylloglossum.*

Lycopodium (Figure 4·17), a genus of some 180 species, is world-wide in distribution. It occurs in arctic, temperate, and tropical regions but is more common as an epiphyte in tropical and subtropical forests. Fossils (called *Lycopodites*) similar to *Lycopodium* have been described as far back as Upper Devonian deposits. The monotypic *Phylloglossum* is closely related to *Lycopodium* and is restricted in distribution to parts of Australia, Tasmania, and New Zealand. There is no fossil record of *Phylloglossum.* Both *Isoetes* and *Stylites* closely

Figure 4·17. Lycopodium lucidulum, portion of a plant. The aerial branches arise from rhizomes.

resemble and are closely related to each other. The over fifty species of *Isoetes* are plants of wet places, and may grow submersed in margins of lakes and ponds and in wet meadows chiefly in temperate regions. Commonly called quillwort, the general form of *Isoetes,* with its strap-shaped leaves, resembles that of chives or onions. *Stylites,* with only two species, has been found only in the high Peruvian mountains where it grows on margins of lakes. *Isoetes* fossils have been found in strata back to the Lower Cretaceous. Both *Isoetes* and *Stylites* are thought to represent stages in reduction in a series from fossil lycopsids like *Pleuro-*

meia and *Nathorstiana* (see Delevoryas, 1963). *Selaginella* (Figure 4·18), with over 600 species, is the largest genus of extant lycopsids. Most species occur in the tropics, usually on soil in wet, humid places. *Selaginellites,* fossils similar in form to *Selaginella,* have been found in deposits of Carboniferous age.

Figure 4·18. *Selaginella bigelovii,* portion of a plant.

What happened during the Permian to result in the extinction of such large numbers of the coal swamp flora? Evidence from the geologic record indicates that there was increasing aridity and widespread glaciation. Swamps decreased in extent. The large arborescent lycopsids, with a very small amount of xylem relative to the size of the plant, had too inefficient a conducting system. With their roots bathed in water and their crowns in an atmosphere of high relative humidity, the arborescent coal swamp lycopsids were well adapted to life in the humid Paleozoic swamps, but were poorly equipped for life under more arid conditions. Smaller herbaceous forms such as *Lycopodium* and *Selaginella* were maintained through time with relatively little change as favorable niches continued to exist.

The lycopsids are often separated into two subgroups, the Ligulatae and Eligulatae, depending on the presence or absence of a *ligule* (Figure 4·21B) on the leaves and sporophylls. Both groups are well represented in the fossil record; extant Ligulatae include *Selaginella, Isoetes,* and *Stylites,* whereas *Lycopodium* and *Phylloglossum* lack ligules. It is of interest that ligulate genera are heterosporous and that the homosporous genera lack ligules. The function of the ligule is still uncertain.

The leaves of some lycopsids, such as *Selaginella* and *Lycopodium* (Figure 4·17, 4·18), are small, although they are long and strap-shaped in *Isoetes* and many arborescent Paleozoic forms. With few exceptions, the leaves possess a single unbranched midvein and there is no leaf gap where the leaf trace passes from the stele; the leaves are descriptively called microphylls. One interpretation is that the leaves of lycopsids evolved from enations. Lycopsid leaves, then, are microphylls in both the phylogenetic and descriptive uses of the word (see Origin of Leaves, Chapter 3).

Stem anatomy is quite variable and will not be discussed in detail. Variation in stelar anatomy in a few species of *Lycopodium* is shown in Figure 3·3. In contrast to the uniformly monostelic condition of *Lycopodium,* some species of *Selaginella* are polystelic, and the separate steles are surrounded by air spaces (Figure 4·19). *Trabeculae,* elongate endodermal cells that traverse the air spaces, hold the steles in position. In extant species secondary growth occurs only in the quillwort *Isoetes* and in *Stylites;* the interested student is referred to the book by Foster and Gifford, 1957, for additional information. In the arborescent fossil plants such as *Lepidodendron* and *Sigillaria* very little vascular tissue was produced during secondary growth. Instead a thick periderm formed (see Secondary Growth, Chapter 3) that also served for support.

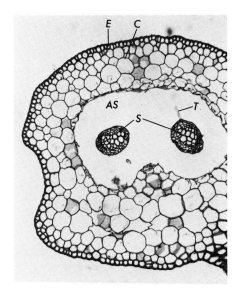

Figure 4·19. *Selaginella* **stem cross section.** The two steles are held in position by trabeculae (only fragments of which are seen in section). Air space (AS), cortex (C), epidermis (E), steles (S), trabecula (T).

The roots are adventitious in origin, arising from pericycle tissue of the stele, as is usual for roots. Roots of *Lycopodium* are initiated close behind the shoot apex and often grow within the cortex for considerable distances before emergence from the stem into the ground.

In lycopsids the sporangia are closely associated with leaflike structures called *sporophylls* (Figure 4·20). Sporangia are borne singly on the adaxial surface of sporophylls, in their axils or on the stem immediately above them. In some lycopsids the sporangia and sporophylls are aggregated to form cones or *strobili* (sing., *strobilus*) (Figure 4·20). In others the sporangia and sporophylls are scattered along the stem amid the leaves.

Lycopodium produces sporangia and spores all of one type (Figure 4·20A, 4·21A). The genus is comprised of homosporous plants, and monoecious gametophytes with multiflagellate sperm develop from the germinated spores. The gametophytes either are subterranean and achlorophyllous or grow at the soil surface and are green. An endo-

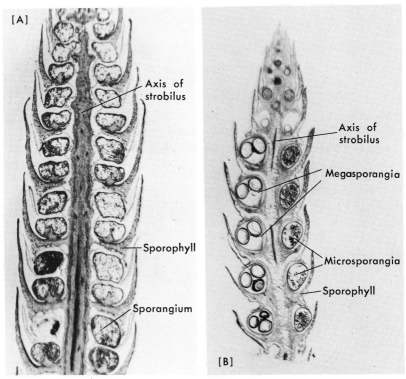

Figure 4·20. Longisections of lycopsid strobili. A: *Lycopodium.* Sporangia and spores are all of one type. **B:** *Selaginella.* Megasporangia with megaspores and microsporangia with microspores.

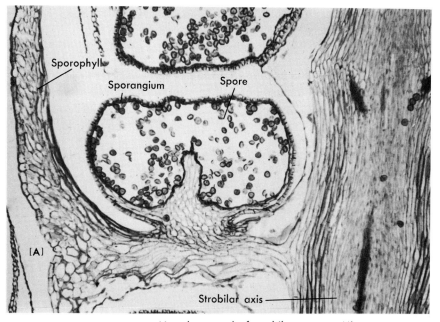

[A]

Sporophyll

Sporangium

Spore

Strobilar axis

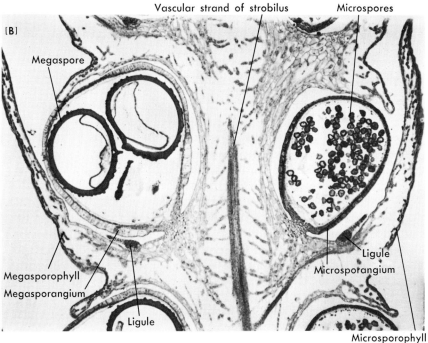

Vascular strand of strobilus

Microspores

[B]

Megaspore

Ligule

Microsporangium

Megasporophyll

Megasporangium

Ligule

Microsporophyll

Figure 4·21. Higher magnification of segments of strobili. A: *Lycopodium*. Ligules absent. B: *Selaginella*. Ligules present and note difference in size between megaspores and microspores.

phytic fungus is a normal symbiont in both types. Spores can be germinated under sterile conditions in the laboratory and the gametophytes can be cultured free from the fungus. The resulting gametophytes, although they often do not closely resemble in morphology those of the same species found in the field with endophytic fungi present, produce sporophytes sexually and apogamously, depending on the environmental conditions (Freeberg and Wetmore, 1957) (Figure 4·22).

Figure 4·22. *Lycopodium selago*. Apogamous outgrowth of the sporophyte from a gametophyte grown in culture. [Photo courtesy of Dr. John A. Freeberg.]

The heterosporous *Selaginella* produces both megasporangia and microsporangia (see also discussion under Homospory, Heterospory, and the Seed, Chapter 3) on the same plant (Figure 4·20B, 4·21B). The small microspores give rise to micro- or male gametophytes (Figure 3·13). Each male gametophyte develops a single antheridium and produces biflagellate sperm. (A review of sperm chemotaxis, Chapter 2, might be useful at this time.) The somewhat larger megagametophyte produces several archegonia (Figure 3·13). Fertilization in some species can occur when the megagametophyte is still retained within the megasporangium. More commonly, however, the megagametophyte is discharged from the sporangium prior to fertilization. Embryo development is rapid and a sporeling soon appears. The seedlike structure of fossil lycopsids was discussed briefly in Chapter 3.

To summarize the major characteristics of this group, the lycopsids characteristically have roots, stems, and leaves (microphylls), and the sporangia are borne singly at the base of or on the adaxial surface of scalelike sporophylls.

The earliest known sphenopsids are found in Lower Devonian strata. They flourished in the later Paleozoic, reaching their peak in both size and diversity in the Carboniferous and Permian. Remains of arborescent forms (e.g., *Calamites*) and herbaceous species (e.g., *Sphenophyllum*) are common in many coal deposits. A rapid decline occurred at the close of the Paleozoic and only a single genus *Equisetum* with some 25 to 30 species is extant today. *Equisetum*, or horsetails, a genus of herbaceous plants, is remarkably similar to fossils placed in the genus *Equisetites*, which in turn has been traced back through the geologic record to the Pennsylvanian Period. *Equisetum* represents a very ancient group of plants that has undergone strikingly little evolutionary modification through time.

The sphenopsids are a distinct phylogenetic line of vascular plants with a characteristic pattern of organization that became established early in their evolution. The main features are (1) small leaves arranged in whorls at the nodes and (2) sporangia borne on structures called *sporangiophores*. There is no evidence to indicate that the sphenopsids gave rise to any other group of land plants.

Because it is the only living representative of this ancient group of plants, *Equisetum* will be emphasized in the remaining part of this section. Widely distributed, *Equisetum* shows greatest morphological variation in the Northern Hemisphere. It often is found in damp places, such as along streams and in marshy areas, but some species thrive in dry habitats. For example, *E. arvense* commonly occurs along well-drained railroad embankments. Most temperate zone species rarely exceed 1 to 1.5 m in height, although *E. hyemale* may attain heights of over 2 m. The tallest is the tropical *E. giganteum* of Mexico and Central America with heights of over 6 m. The slender stems (less than 2.5 cm in diameter) of *E. giganteum* are supported by the lush adjacent tropical vegetation.

The most conspicuous feature of the vegetative plant is the ridged stem bearing whorled leaves. The branches, when present, are also in whorls (Figure 4·23). However, the branch primordia are not axillary, but are alternate with the leaves. The main photosynthetic part of the plant is the stem; the leaves are small, scalelike, and in some species achlorophyllous. The leaves of *Equisetum* are microphyllous in that there is a single unbranched midvein and the vascular trace does not leave a gap in the stele. However, many early sphenopsids had more extensive vasculature in the leaves and one current interpretation is that the leaves of the sphenopsids evolved by modification of a small branch system. The leaves, therefore, evolved from telomes, not ena-

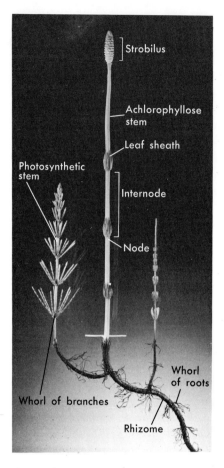

Figure 4·23. *Equisetum arvense.* Growth habit. Note whorls of leaves, branches, and roots and terminal strobilus. In this species the strobilus develops at the apex of an ephemeral, achlorophyllose stem. [Courtesy of the Field Museum of Natural History, Chicago, Illinois.]

tions. The stem is segmented into well-defined nodes and internodes. The whorled leaves are laterally fused and form a sheath about the stem; the leaf tips remain free. Because of the pattern of cell initiation, the young stems are readily disarticulated at the nodes. In addition to a large functioning apical cell at the apex of each stem (Figure 4·24), there is a center of active cell division (an intercalary meristem) at the lower end of each internode. This meristematic zone is protected by the overarching leaf sheath and the disarticulation occurs across these thin-walled cells of the meristem. The intercalary meristem is active for a period of time but ceases activity with maturation of the stem segment. Most of the cells of the internode arise from the activity of the intercalary meristem.

The anatomy of the aerial stem resembles that of marsh plants in the presence of numerous canals (Figure 4·25A). In the stem center a large *central* or *pith canal* is surrounded by remains of the pith. The *carinal canals* form a ring to the exterior of the central canal and mark the positions of the protoxylem poles (Figure 4·25B). The metaxylem and phloem lie to the exterior of the protoxylem. A well-defined endodermis separates the stele from the cortex. In the cortex a third system of canals, the *vallecular canals*, are found. All three canal systems extend the length of each internode, but do not cross the node, which consists of a solid diaphragm of tissue. There the discrete strands of xylem and phloem join to form a solid siphonostele. The presence of numerous air canals even in those species that today grow in relatively dry conditions is thought to indicate that *Equisetum* evolved from ancestors that were adapted to marshy or swampy environments. The ridges of the stem are readily apparent in sectioned material (Figure 4·25A). The cell walls of the ridges are greatly thickened and are usually strongly silicified. The silica, absent from most commercially available slides, is evident in hand sections of living material (Figure 4·25C). These siliceous ridges made possible the use of species of *Equisetum* for scouring pots, pans, and dishes in colonial days in America. The aerial stems arise from often deep-seated underground rhizomes (Figure 4·23). Rhizome anatomy has the same basic structure as the aerial stems. All roots, except the primary root of the embryo, are adventitious in origin and arise in whorls at the nodes of rhizomes or the under-

Apical cell   Leaf primordium

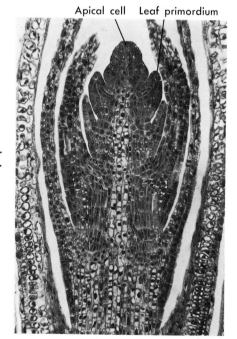

Figure 4·24. *Equisetum hyemale*. Median longisection of shoot apex. A single apical cell is present.

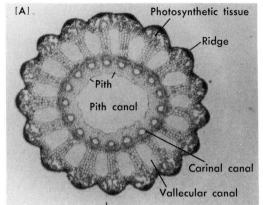

[A] Photosynthetic tissue
Ridge
Pith
Pith canal
Carinal canal
Vallecular canal

Figure 4·25. Equisetum. A: E. arvense. Cross section of stem. **B: E. arvense.** Higher magnification to show location of protoxylem, metaxylem, and phloem. **C:** Photo of *E. laevigatum* to show siliceous tubercles of the stem ridges. [**C** courtesy of Dane D. Hardin.]

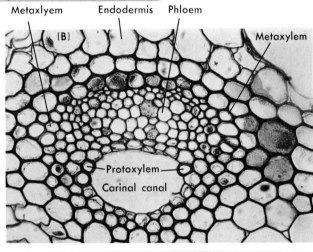

Metaxlyem   Endodermis   Phloem
[B]   Metaxylem
Protoxylem
Carinal canal

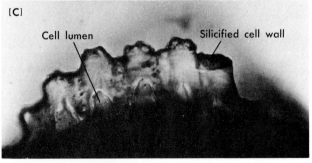

[C]
Cell lumen   Silicified cell wall

ground parts of aerial stems. A longitudinal section of a root tip of *Equisetum hyemale* is shown in Figure 3·10.

Some species of *Equisetum* are persistent weeds in gardens and fields. Their deep-seated rhizomes (5 to 6 ft deep in some species) coupled with the presence of preformed branch and root primordia at each node make the plant difficult to eradicate once established. Because of the preformed primordia each node-internode segment of the aerial stem or rhizome has the potentiality of giving rise to a new plant. These preformed branch primordia are present even in the normally unbranched species, and a few lateral branches often develop on stems of normally unbranched plants in which the apex of the stem has been injured. Released from hormonal inhibition, one or more branch primordia rapidly grow out through the leaf sheath. Root primordia are always associated with branches, and *Equisetum* is unique in that

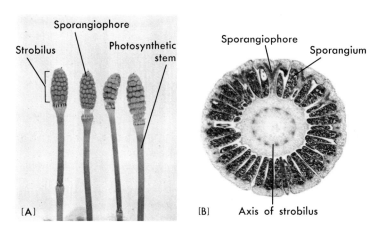

Figure 4·26. A: *Equisetum laevigatum*. Strobili develop at the tips of photosynthetic stems. **B: *Equisetum sp*.** Cross section of strobilus to show peltate sporangiophores bearing sporangia.

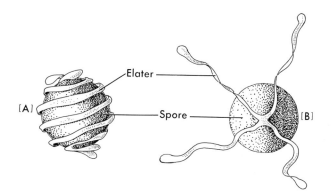

Figure 4·27. *Equisetum hyemale*. Spores with elaters. A: Moist condition with elaters tightly coiled around the spore. **B:** Dry with elaters uncoiled. The elaters, in the uncoiled position, serve to decrease the rate of descent of the spore upon discharge from the sporangium.

the base of every branch, whether developed or quiescent, is provided with a root primordium.

The sporangia are localized in strobili, borne at the tips of normally photosynthetic branches in some (Figure 4·26A) or at the tips of achlorophyllous stems in others (Figure 4·23). The strobilar axis bears a number of peltate sporangiophores, which, in turn bear five or more elongate sporangia (Figure 4·26B). Meiosis and spore formation occur within the sporangia. At maturity the elongation of the strobilar axis results in the sporangiophores pulling away from each other. Sporangial dehiscence occurs along preformed lines of weakness and the spores are liberated. Strobilar elongation often proceeds from base to tip.

Figure 4·28. *Equisetum arvense*. Gametophyte from a single spore culture bearing a sporophyte developed following self-fertilization.

The spores of *Equisetum* are unique among contemporary plants in the possession of attached appendages called elaters (Figure 4·27). (Note that the elaters of *Equisetum* are not comparable to those structures by the same name found in liverwort and hornwort sporangia.) The elaters are sensitive to moisture changes, unwinding and winding upon drying and wetting, respectively. Elaterate spores are not common in the fossil record. As might be expected, they occur in species of *Equisetites,* but apparently even here not all species had them. Spores with attached elaters have been reported only in one other plant, a Middle Pennsylvanian sphenopsid with three elaters. Baxter and Leisman (1967) found that the coiled elaters on spores of this plant released by maceration from coal balls had retained their ability to expand and contract after approximately 290 million years of preservation.

The homosporous spores of *Equisetum* germinate rapidly on suitable substrates, giving rise to small gametophytes from several to 10 mm or more in diameter (Figure 4·28). The gametophytes are anchored to the substrate by colorless, unicellular rhizoids. The thallus usually consists of a parenchymatous basal cushion from which arise membranous richly chlorophyllous outgrowths. The archegonia develop in the parenchymatous basal cushion either of the same plants that bear antheridia or of different plants. The antheridia are embedded in short club-shaped outgrowths or in the membranous outgrowths from the basal cushion. Following fertilization by a multiflagellate sperm (Figure 2·3B), the zygote gives rise to an embryo with essentially the same organization as the adult plant (Figure 4·29).

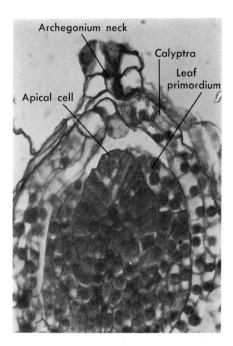

Figure 4·29. *Equisetum telmateia.* **Embryo sporophyte within the archegonium.**

The spores are relatively thin-walled and dry out rapidly. Viability for many is less than fourteen days, although refrigeration can extend their life span. The gametophytes are also susceptible to rapid desiccation. Although gametophytes with young sporophytes have been found in nature, it is likely that vegetative reproduction is more important in maintaining populations and in colonizing new habitats than are spores. The existence of preformed root and branch primordia certainly speeds the development of new plants from detached stem segments.

The identification of hybrids of *Equisetum* in both Europe and North America is evidence that sexual reproduction occurs and can lead to the establishment of new populations. However the hybrids reproduce primarily if not entirely by vegetative means, because meiosis is irregular and the spores generally are achlorophyllous and aborted. An exception to the preceding statement is one hybrid population in Santa Cruz, California, in which a small fraction (less than 1 per cent) of the spores contain chlorophyll at maturity and in which a small proportion of these green spores have been shown to be capable of germination (Hardin and Doyle, unpublished).

Ferns

The ferns, like the other higher cryptogams, are geologically an ancient group of plants. The ferns, with about 10,000 species, are a smaller group than are the mosses (with about 14,000 species), but because of their size, fern diversity is more striking. Ferns range in size from the tropical tree ferns to small aquatic plants less than 2 cm in length. Although several of the fern groups have changed little with time (e.g., members of the family Osmundaceae), other groups (e.g., Polypodiaceae) seem to be undergoing active speciation. Most extant ferns are relatively small herbaceous plants. Among contemporary ferns, secondary growth has been reported only in *Botrychium;* even tree ferns consist entirely of primary tissue.

The sporophyte is the dominant generation and most of the diversity in form and structure occurs in this growth phase. Only a brief description of the salient features of the more common ferns will be given here. Additional information can be found in any one of a number of morphology texts.

Ferns are characteristically megaphyllous; that is, they have large leaves with a well-developed venation system and the leaf trace is associated with a well-defined leaf gap where the trace leaves the stele. Evidence in the fossil record indicates that the fern leaf (or *frond*) evolved by the modification of a large lateral branch system. The frond is the most conspicuous part of the sporophyte. It may be simple, with an undivided blade, or compound. Each major subdivision of the compound leaf is called a *pinna,* and the pinna, in turn, may be further subdivided. The fronds are borne scattered along a rhizome, growing at or below the soil surface, or are crowded at the apex of a short stem (Figure 4·30). In many ferns of the temperate region the fronds are annual, with a new set developed each year. The young frond exhibits apical growth; in some cases apical activity continues for several years

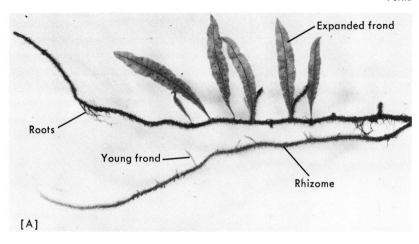

Expanded frond

Roots

Young frond

Rhizome

[A]

Frond

[B]

Figure 4·30. A: *Polypodium lycopodioides.* Fronds arise scattered along a rhizome. **B: *Asplenium bulbiferum.*** Fronds arise near the apex of a short, erect stem.

(e.g., the perennial leaf of *Lygodium* may reach a length of over 32 m). The young fern frond has a characteristic pattern of unrolling during development, called *circinate vernation* (Figure 4·31A). Among the other extant plants circinate vernation also occurs in leaf development of cycads (gymnospermous seed plants).

Anatomically, the stem is usually complex. The vascular cylinder generally is a highly dissected protostele or, more commonly, a siphonostele. The complex stem anatomy is associated with the development of leaf traces and leaf gaps. The xylem characteristically contains tracheids only, although vessel elements occur in the bracken fern *Pteridium aquilinum* and in the water fern *Marsilea*. Adventitious roots generally develop along the rhizome in close association with the leaf bases or at the base of the erect stem.

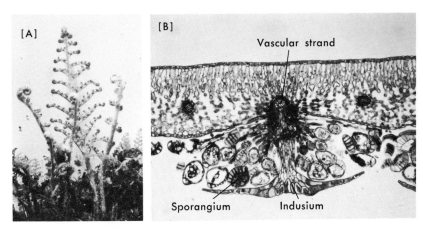

Figure 4·31. A: *Polystichum setiferum*. Young leaves show circinate vernation. **B: *Cyrtomium sp*.** Section of leaf through a sorus to show the relationship of the indusium and sporangia to the leaf.

The sporangia develop at the margins or the abaxial surface of the leaves or on specialized segments of some of the fronds. In many ferns the brownish sporangia occur in clusters; each cluster of sporangia is called a *sorus* (pl., *sori*). The sori are borne exposed on the abaxial surface of the leaf in some ferns, but more commonly the sori are protected by leaf tissue of some kind. An outgrowth of leaf tissue called an *indusium* (Figure 4·31B) covers the sorus in many ferns and protects the sporangia from drying out. In some ferns (such as the maidenhair fern, *Adiantum*) the inrolled leaf margin called a *false indusium* protects the sporangia. In still other ferns the sporangia are embedded in tissue of specialized segments of some fronds. The position of the sporangia on the leaf and the shape of the indusium are important characteristics in fern identification (Figure 4·32).

The sporangium of the advanced fern families is a highly differentiated structure with a remarkable mechanism for spore discharge (Figure 4·33). In these ferns the sides of the lens-shaped sporangium

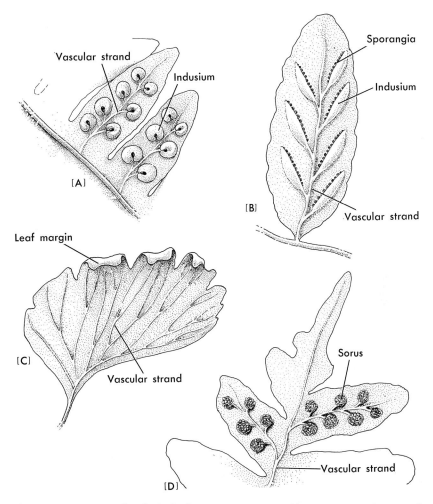

Figure 4·32. Sori and indusia in ferns. A: *Dryopteris.* The sporangia are covered by a shield-shaped indusium. **B:** *Asplenium.* An elongate indusium is present. **C:** *Adiantum.* The leaf margin (a false indusium) covers the sporangia. **D:** *Polypodium.* The sporangia are borne naked on the lower surface of the frond.

consist of thin-walled flattened cells. The *annulus,* a row of cells with their walls thickened on the innermost and radial sides, extends from the stalk over the top of the sporangium. A row of thin-walled cells, including two *lip cells,* connect the annulus with the stalk on the other side (Figure 4·33A). In the mature sporangium the cells of the annulus are filled with water prior to spore discharge. Water loss by evaporation results in the pulling in of the unthickened sides of the cells of the annulus. The resultant decrease in volume of these cells sets up strains in such a direction that a rupture occurs between the two lip cells and across the sides of the sporangium (Figure 4·33B). Continued water loss causes the unthickened sides of the annulus cells to be pulled in farther and farther, and the annulus bends slowly backward carrying the spore-filled half of the sporangium with it. The thickened walls of the annulus cells are under increasing tension, but the annulus is prevented from returning to its original position because of the great cohesive force of the water molecules and the even greater adhesive force between the water molecules and the cell walls. During continued evaporation, a point is ultimately reached where the cohesive force of water is exceeded and the water column suddenly breaks to give a gas phase. Breaking the water column in one cell triggers a nearly instantaneous reaction in the other cells of the annulus, and the spores are hurled 2 cm or more away as the sporangium snaps back to its original shape. (See Ingold, 1965, for a fascinating account of spore discharge mechanisms in fungi, bryophytes, and ferns.)

The discharged spore germinates within several days upon landing on a suitable substrate and a short filament grows out through the ruptured spore coat. The plane of cell division soon changes so that a dorsiventrally flattened gametophyte, the *prothallus,* develops (Figure 3·12). The prothallus is potentially perennial, although it is often annual in the field because of its sensitivity to desiccation. The prothallus consists of a thickened midrib and unistratose lateral wings. Colorless unicellular rhizoids anchor the prothallus to the substrate and cell initiation occurs at the base of the apical notch. Antheridia and archegonia are borne on the lower surface of the prothallus, next to the soil. Antheridial initiation characteristically begins in advance of archegonial formation, with the result that the antheridia often are found on the older parts of the prothallus, scattered among the rhizoids. Archegonia develop on the cushion of tissue immediately behind the

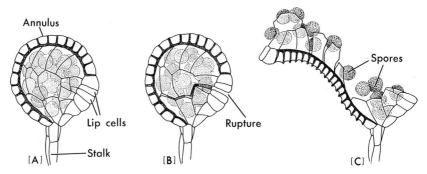

Figure 4·33. Sporangium and sporangial dehiscence in the fern, *Polypodium sp.*

Annulus · Lip cells · Stalk · [A] · [B] · Rupture · Spores · [C]

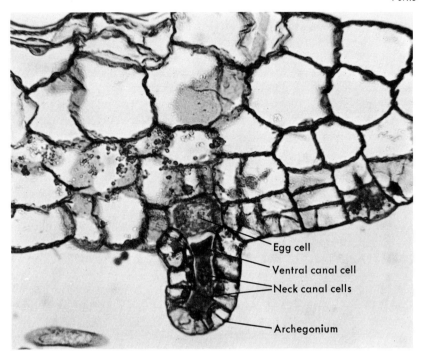

Egg cell

Ventral canal cell

Neck canal cells

Archegonium

Figure 4·34. Nearly mature fern archegonium. The venter is embedded in mid-rib tissue.

apical notch and the venter of the archegonium is embedded in this cushion (Figure 4·34). The neck of the archegonium is bent back toward the base of the prothallus, toward the antheridia. This orientation of the archegonial neck is thought to enhance the frequency of self-fertilization in these monoecious plants (see Chapter 3). Chemotaxis of the multiflagellate sperm was discussed in Chapter 2.

The zygote begins development soon after fertilization and the root and stem primordia and the primordium of the first leaf differentiate early during embryogeny. The embryo does not undergo a period of dormancy and the young fern plant soon grows out and establishes independence. The prothallus generally withers and dies during the early establishment of the young sporophyte.

Although most of the ferns are homosporous, five genera of extant heterosporous ferns are known. The heterosporous ferns usually occur in wet, marshy places (e.g., *Masilea*), or they float on bodies of water (e.g., *Salvinia* and *Azolla*). The closeness of the relationship between the heterosporous and the homosporous ferns is still unclear.

Summary

The definitive characteristics used to delimit the Classes of higher cryptogams come mainly from the sporophytic growth phase. The organography of the sporophyte and the relationship of the sporangium to the other plant parts are of particular importance. Gametophytic characteristics are of less importance at this level of classification, mainly because the form and structure of the gametophytes vary so markedly within a single class. A summary of the salient features of plants in each group of higher cryptogams follows.

BRYOPSIDA. Gametophyte the conspicuous generation; sporophyte leafless and rootless; water-conducting cells not lignified; sporangium terminal; homosporous (but some are functionally heterosporous); biflagellate sperm.

Hornworts. Sporophyte with intercalary meristem; spore maturation proceeds from tip to base of capsule; elaters intermixed with spores; thalloid gametophytes dorsiventrally flattened; chloroplasts in some species with pyrenoids; unicellular rhizoids.

Liverworts. Sporophyte development by diffuse pattern of cell division (as opposed to a localized meristem) and over-all differentiation; stomata absent; elaters or other nonmeiotic cells intermixed with spores; with few exceptions both thalloid and leafy forms dorsiventrally flattened; unicellular rhizoids.

Mosses. Sporophyte with apical growth; capsule with peristome (except in reduced forms); no elaters or other nonmeiotic cells intermixed with spores; leafy gametophyte usually radially symmetrical; multicellular rhizoids.

PSILOPSIDA. Sporophyte the conspicuous generation; roots absent; lateral appendages present or absent, when present the leaflike appendages probably evolved from enations; leaf gap absent; water-conducting cells lignified; sporangium terminal or lateral; homosporous; multiflagellate sperm.

LYCOPSIDA. Sporophyte the conspicuous generation; root, stem, and leaf present; the leaf (microphyll) probably evolved from an enation; leaf gap absent; water-conducting cells lignified; sporangium in or near axil of leaf (sporophyll); both homosporous and heterosporous plants; bi- and multiflagellate sperm.

SPHENOPSIDA. Sporophyte the conspicuous generation; root, stem, and leaf present; leaves probably evolved from a small lateral branch system; leaf gap absent; water-conducting cells lignified; stem articulated with whorled leaves and lateral branches (when present) ; sporangia borne on sporangiophores; spores with elaters in *Equisetum,* but elaters absent in most genera; homosporous and heterosporous; multiflagellate sperm.

PTEROPSIDA. Sporophyte the conspicuous generation; root, stem, and leaf present; leaf evolved from a large lateral branch system (megaphyll) ; leaf gap present; frond the dominant part of the sporophyte; water-conducting cells lignified ; sporangia borne on leaf margin, or on abaxial surface of leaf, or embedded in modified leaf segments; homosporous and heterosporous (rare) ; multiflagellate sperm.

It might be useful to close this chapter on diversity with a statement on unity, by reviewing the features these plants have in common. They have (1) embryos protected by a multicellular maternal plant, (2) a similar type of life cycle, (3) a cuticle, (4) stomata (except the liverworts), (5) multicellular gametangia (archegonia and antheridia), and (6) multicellular sporangia. Although some of these characteristics could have resulted from convergent evolution, it is unlikely that the stoma with its two highly differentiated guard cells evolved more than once during plant evolution. The higher cryptogams are considered to be closely related to each other, in spite of the amount of diversity between the groups described here. There is no compelling evidence that plants in any class of higher cryptogams gave rise through evolution to plants in any other group. The progenitors of plants in each class have not yet been identified, if they ever will be, in the fossil record.

Special Topics

IN THIS CHAPTER selected topics which merit special consideration will be discussed. Most of the topics concern aspects of development in which there is active research. Therefore this chapter should be considered a progress report in which the most interesting part of the research is not yet finished.

The spore and the zygote represent two stages in the life cycle where the cell number is reduced to the minimum. Development is the process by which the spore and the zygote through successive cell divisions give rise to the characteristic organization of the multicellular haploid and diploid growth phases of the higher cryptogams. Cell differentiation and the differentiation of tissues and organs are included in the general concept of development.

In recent years there has been an increasing appreciation of environmental factors in the regulation of expression of the genetic potential of the cell in plant development. The extranuclear environment is rarely constant in all its parameters. Temperature, light intensity, and moisture and nutrient availability undergo daily and seasonal change. Concentrations of dissolved oxygen and carbon dioxide in cells change with time. Moreover, nutritional and hormonal gradients may change quantitatively and qualitatively during growth of the plant. There are two important aspects of the study of how an environmental stimulus induces a specific pattern of development. One concerns the level of control: whether the stimulus works in the nucleus at the level of gene activation (derepression) and transcription or in the cytoplasm at the level of translation. The second aspect is clarification of the process by which transcription and translation lead to cellular change.

A major characteristic of developing systems is that once a cell embarks on a particular pathway of development, it will continue along this pathway until new signals are received; cells react to a changing environment, as indicated earlier. It is also important to note that the cell must be in the proper physiological state in order for the signal to induce a change in developmental pathways. Several events in the development of higher cryptogams have been selected for discussion in the following sections.

Spore Germination

The unicellular, haploid spore carries the genetic potential for the development of the gametophyte (and of the sporophyte as well). As pointed out in Chapter 2, the spore is highly specialized in its function, representing the end of one developmental sequence and the beginning of a new one. The spore represents a period of suspended growth in the life of the organism. Developing as it does after meiosis, the spore may carry with it new gene combinations with the potential for better adaptation of the organism to the environment. Spores may also function to disperse the species to new geographic locations. An important characteristic of spores is their ability to remain dormant under certain environmental conditions and to germinate under others.

In general, spore *dormancy* is the period of low metabolic activity between maturation and germination of the spore. The length of time that spores remain dormant before viability decreases is variable, being measured in days or weeks in some plants and in tens of years in others. Spores that are green at maturity often have a higher metabolic rate and a shorter viability than do those that are nongreen. Not all spores have a dormant period. Some germinate immediately upon maturation as in the liverworts *Pellia* and *Conocephalum*. In these plants the spores usually germinate prior to capsule dehiscence, and multicellular "spores" are discharged.

Spore *activation* is the application of a stimulus that leads to germination. This activation is influenced by a number of interacting factors, including temperature, light (quality, intensity, and photoperiod), growth substances, and mechanical treatment.

Germination is the process by which a spore is changed from the dormant state to one of high metabolic activity. The process is (arbitrarily) culminated with the appearance of the first irreversible stage that is phenotypically different from the dormant stage. In the higher cryptogams the emergence of the germ tube, the rhizoid, or the prothallus is the morphological manifestation of germination and is the end result of the germination process (Figure 5·1). Imbibition of water,

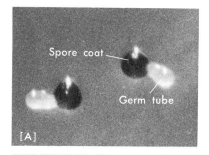

Figure 5·1. *Sphaerocarpos cristatus*. A: Spore germination. **B:** Young sporeling.

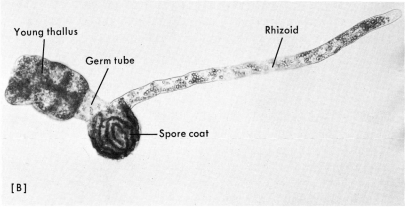

with consequent swelling of the spore and rupture of the spore exine, is one of the early stages in the germination process. The intine does not rupture, but is continuous with the wall of the germ tube or rhizoid. A whole series of biochemical reactions occur between the onset of water uptake and outgrowth of the young plant, or sporeling, from the spore. The biochemical reactions involved in the germination process in the higher cryptogams, in contrast to spore germination in fungi and bacteria, have been little studied.

Most of the experimental work on spore germination is of two kinds: (1) spore activation and (2) establishment of polarity during germination. These topics will be discussed separately.

SPORE ACTIVATION

A few of the factors which influence the timing of germination have already been discussed. In addition, the timing of germination may be modified by several other factors: (1) the type of medium upon which the spores are sown, including its osmolarity, concentrations of specific ions in the medium and pH of the medium; (2) the environment in which the sporophyte, and therefore the spores, develop; and (3) the age of the spores. For reasons not yet understood, recently matured spores usually germinate more rapidly than do older ones. As an example, spores of the moss *Physcomitrium piriforme* still viable after fifty-five years of storage, required a few weeks to germinate, whereas freshly collected spores of the same species germinated within three days (Paschke, 1965).

Chemical control (inhibition) of spore germination is known to occur. The arresting substances may come either from the maternal plant or from the spore itself. For example, mature spores of the liverwort *Sphaerocarpos donnellii* do not germinate as long as the sporophyte capsule (the sporangium) is attached to the living plant. When the spores are liberated from the capsule and are placed on an agar medium, or even when the intact capsule containing spores is placed on agar, germination occurs in a short period of time. Comparable spores in capsules left attached to the intact maternal plant remain dormant. The chemical inhibitors, whether coming from the maternal plant or from the spores themselves, presumably function to prevent immediate germination, thus limiting the time of germination to the next growing season. According to this interpretation, chemical inhibition of spore germination could be considered an adaptation to the seasonal characteristics of the environment in which these plants normally grow. However, the correlative mechanism by which growth is inhibited is unknown.

A few examples are known in which the spore coat itself influences the timing of germination. Whether this restriction is due to mechanical restraint or to a permeability barrier is still to be determined. These restraints probably delay germination at least until the next growing season. In nature the spore coat of these species is apparently altered by the abrasive action of the soil particles, by freezing and thawing, or by microbial activity. In the laboratory, germination of thick-walled spores of certain species of *Lycopodium* has been brought about by treating the spores with concentrated sulfuric acid or by grinding them with sand.

The spores of higher cryptogams usually need light for germination. This generalization, however, is not without exceptions. In many species some spores do germinate in the dark, although there is a distinct reduction in the per cent that germinate or a delay in germination compared to spore germination in the light. The majority of spores of these species, however, remain dormant. In the bryophytes especially, appreciable dark germination (shown again by Hoffman, 1964, for the moss *Funaria hygrometrica*) occurs only when sugars such as glucose are present in the medium. The adaptive value of dark germination for normally photosynthetic organisms might be questioned.

However, sporelings usually exhibit negative geotropic behavior in the dark and positive phototropic responses in weak illumination. If the spores are not buried too deeply, subterranean sporelings most likely grow up and around soil particles in the dark or in dim illumination until the soil surface is reached. Of course, the normal life of some gametophytes (such as those of *Psilotum,* of some species of *Lycopodium,* and of the liverwort *Cryptothallus*) is heterotrophic and subterranean and presumably the spores of these plants are able to germinate in the dark.

Spores of many species have a light requirement for germination. In some cases light is needed to stimulate imbibition of water; in others it is needed to induce the outgrowth of the sporeling following uptake of water. Only a brief account of the influence of light on germination will be presented here. In addition to the general review by Sussman (1965), the interested student should refer to the excellent work on the light control of germination of moss spores by the Finnish researcher Valanne (1966).

A photoperiodic requirement for spore germination has been reported by some workers. However, many of these investigators have not always separated satisfactorily the effects of photoperiod from that of a response to total available energy. Under equivalent light intensity plants grown in short-day regimes receive less total radiant energy per daily cycle than do plants grown in long-day regimes. Light intensities should be adjusted so that plants grown in different day lengths receive equivalent amounts of total energy during each light cycle. Adjustment of light intensities has not always been done. For this reason much of the work on photoperiodism needs to be repeated.

Well-documented effects of light quality on spore germination are present in the literature. The liverwort *Sphaerocarpos cristatus* and the bracken fern *Pteridium aquilinum* are among the few plants with spores that apparently germinate under all wavelengths of the visible spectrum. Spores of most plants, however, exhibit a differential response to the different wavelengths. Red light generally is the most effective in promoting germination; blue, green, and far-red wavelengths often delay or inhibit germination. In contrast to *S. cristatus,* mentioned earlier, maximum germination in *S. donnellii* occurs in both blue and far-red light, whereas red light has almost no effect (Mohr, 1963).

The reversible red–far-red system, the same system that controls many morphogenetic events in seed plants, has been shown to control spore germination in some species of higher cryptogams (Figure 5·2). Spores activated by a short exposure to red light (660 nm) and then placed in the dark yield a higher per cent germination than do those of the dark control not exposed to red light. Application of a short period

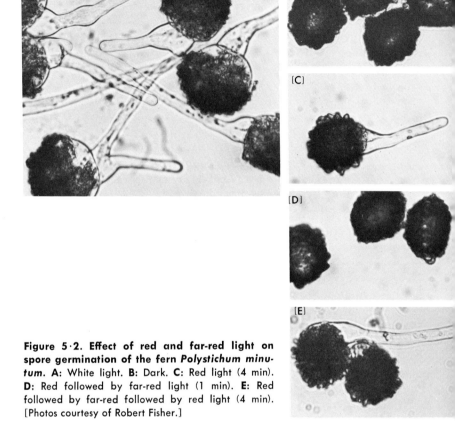

Figure 5·2. Effect of red and far-red light on spore germination of the fern *Polystichum minutum*. A: White light. **B:** Dark. **C:** Red light (4 min). **D:** Red followed by far-red light (1 min). **E:** Red followed by far-red followed by red light (4 min). [Photos courtesy of Robert Fisher.]

of far-red irradiation (730 nm) immediately following the exposure to red light substantially reduces the per cent germination. Far-red light cancels the promotive effect of red light. When spores sequentially exposed to first red and then far-red light are again given a brief exposure to red light, the per cent germination is found to be as high as if the spores had never been exposed to the interval of far-red light (Table 5·1).

The effects of red and far-red light are reversible and the germination response depends on the quality of light during the final light treatment. These results are fully in keeping with results obtained, for example, in the classic studies on lettuce seed germination (see Hendricks and Borthwick, 1954). In those fern species that do possess this pigment system, red light induces the outgrowth of the germ tube; far-red

TABLE 5·1
Response (swelling of spore with rupture of the
exine and greening of the chloroplasts) of spores
of *Funaria hygrometrica* to red (R) and far-red
(FR) light (after Bauer and Mohr, 1959)

LIGHT TREATMENT	PER CENT RESPONSE
Dark control	48 ± 0.7
R (3 hr)	82 ± 0.6
R (3 hr) + FR (5 min)	64 ± 1.0
R + FR + R (5 min)	85 ± 1.0

light inhibits this event. In contrast, only the first stage in germination (imbibition of water, rupture of the exine, and greening of the spore) is induced by red light and is reversed by far-red light in the moss *Funaria hygrometrica* (Bauer and Mohr, 1959).

There is little doubt that the photoreceptive pigment in the red–far-red light response is phytochrome, a bluish-green pigment involved in similar reversible reactions in seed plants. The photoreceptor (or photoreceptors) involved in the response of spores to the other wavelengths of light awaits identification and further study. Filtering effects of the pigments in the spore walls add a complication to these studies.

Ultrastructural changes during spore germination have been studied in the moss *Ceratodon purpureus* by Valanne (1966). She found that changes in the chloroplast and oil bodies were the most noticeable during germination. The ungerminated spore has chloroplasts with a poorly developed thylakoid system, without well-defined grana, and with few starch grains. The oil bodies are angular in outline. Spores that have imbibed water and have swollen in the light contain chloroplasts with an extensive thylakoid development and with differentiation into numerous grana. The starch disappears from the chloroplasts, and the oil bodies, now spherical, show signs of lipid digestion. There is also an increase in the number of chloroplasts. Outgrowth of the germ tube from the spore is preceded by the movement of the chloroplasts and oil bodies toward the side of the spore where the spore exine has ruptured and from which the outgrowth occurs.

The outgrowth of the germ tube in *Ceratodon* requires the presence of light and is controlled by the reversible red–far-red phytochrome-mediated system (Valanne, 1966). Spores that have imbibed water in the dark, like those swollen in the light, show an increase in the number of chloroplasts, and the chloroplasts show an increase in thylakoid development with some differentiation of grana. (Chlorophyll synthesis by dark-grown plants appears to be a widespread phenomenon in bryophytes.) However, development of the thylakoid system is not as great as that of spores swollen in the light. Moreover, spores that have imbibed water in the dark still have starch within the chloroplasts and the oil bodies remain nearly unchanged. Thus the most apparent difference between spores swollen in the light or dark is the inability of the latter to utilize the reserve food stored as starch or lipid. Perhaps this explains why an exogenous supply of simple sugars such as sucrose and glucose promotes the dark germination of many bryophyte spores, including those of *Ceratodon*.

The study of spore germination is still in its infancy, despite many years of investigation. Critical experiments have been done in very few cases so that very little is known about how the environmental stimuli cause a change in the biochemical machinery of the cell which leads to germination. Moreover, studies have just begun on the identification of the metabolic pathways that operate in the dormant spores of the higher cryptogams.

INDUCTION OF POLARITY

In many higher cryptogams the place of emergence of the sporeling through the exine is rigidly predetermined, usually by the architecture of the spore coat itself. These are called *polar* spores. In these spores emergence of the sporeling is usually through the triradiate ridge (or proximal or inner) face of the spore which is the face where the four spores were appressed during spore tetrad development (Figure 2·8). The free outer (or distal) face is the place of germ tube emergence in a few plants, such as in species of *Sphaerocarpos*.

Spores in which the place of emergence of the sporeling is not determined by spore coat structure, but by the environment, interest us here. These spores, often called *apolar* spores, make it possible to study the orientation by the environment of cytoplasmic gradients, and with it the establishment of the direction of outgrowth of the sporeling. Establishment of polarity leads to the directed orientation of the mitotic spindle, a phenomenon of great importance in plant morphogenesis. The two daughter cells resulting from an unequal cell division have dissimilar fates during subsequent development.

Most of the experimental work on the orientation of polarity in the higher cryptogams has been done on several species of the horsetail *Equisetum,* the moss *Funaria hygrometrica,* and the ferns *Dryopteris filix-mas* and *Osmunda cinnamomea. Equisetum,* however, has been the favorite research tool. The thin-walled, nearly spherical spores of *Equisetum* contain numerous chloroplasts uniformly distributed around the large, centrally positioned nucleus. Unilateral illumination leads to an asymmetric distribution of the organelles—the chloroplasts move toward the side of the spore with the highest light intensity and the nucleus moves toward the opposite, or darker, side of the spore. Polarity during this period is labile and can be negated or reoriented by a change in the light direction.

Polarity is irreversibly set by the first mitotic division. In *Equisetum* this division occurs about twenty-four hours after the spores are placed upon a suitable medium. Spindle fiber orientation is parallel to the long axis of the cytoplasmic gradient, and the division gives rise to a large cell with many chloroplasts and a smaller one with few chloroplasts. The division is unequal in that it separates the cytoplasm quantitatively, and it provides quite different environments for the two daughter nuclei. The fate of each cell is determined by this unequal division. The smaller cell, which forms on the darker side of the *Equisetum* spore, gives rise to the rhizoid and does not divide again. The larger cell divides repeatedly and gives rise to the prothallus. The more active cell is a meristemoid in the sense of Bünning (1953). The establishment of polarity in apolar spores of ferns and bryophytes is essentially similar to that described for *Equisetum,* except that rhizoids of mosses are capable of repeated cell division. (See the paper by Gantt and Arnott, 1965, for a histochemical and ultrastructural study of spore germination in the ostrich fern, *Matteuccia struthiopteris.*)

Evidence that latent polarity exists in these spores and that a stimulus from the environment only reorients an existing asymmetrical structure comes from studies by Nakazawa (1960). He found that rhizoid formation during germination of spores of *Equisetum arvense* is preceded by the differentiation of a localized region of the cytoplasm and the adjacent cell wall that selectively absorbs metallic ions such as those of nickel and manganese. The metallophilic region appears at the place of rhizoid origin prior to the first mitotic division and the earliest morphological appearance of the rhizoid outgrowth. Centrifugation does not displace the metallophilic region. He also found that a metallophilic region is already present in spores that are freshly discharged from the sporangium and that the rhizoid of dark-germinated sporelings arises at this point. In *Equisetum,* at least, unilateral light appears to reorient a pre-existing asymmetrical structure in the spore, and in so doing induces the formation of a new metallophilic rhizoid point. Thus unilateral light does not induce polarity, but reorients existing polarity. Localized binding of metallic ions also occurs at the site of rhizoid origin in fern spores, such as *Dryopteris,* but apparently not in bryophytes.

Polarotropism (i.e., the response to plane polarized light) in spore germination has been studied by several investigators, and much has been learned about the nature and orientation of the photoreceptor chromophore as a result of these studies. Only phototropically responsive spores respond to polarized light (Bünning and Etzold, 1958). Unless otherwise noted, the plane of vibration refers to the plane of the electric vector. Jaffe (1960) showed that the polarotropic action spectrum corresponds to the phototropic action spectrum and he concluded that the orienting effects of both polarized and unpolarized light are variants of the general phenomenon of phototropism. Positively phototropic cells, such as the photosynthetic chloronema of *Dryopteris, Osmunda, Equisetum,* and *Funaria* (Figure 5·3), grow perpendicular to the vibration plane of polarized light; negatively phototropic cells, such as the unicellular rhizoids of *Dryopteris, Osmunda,* and *Equisetum,* grow parallel to it. The multicellular rhizoids of *Funaria* do not give a clear-cut orientation.

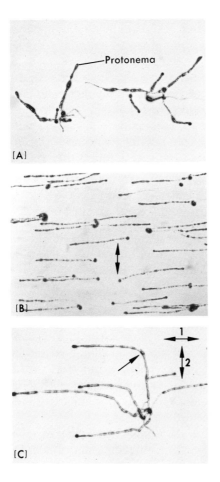

Figure 5·3. Spore germination and protonemal growth of the moss *Funaria hygrometrica* in plane polarized white light. The plane of the electrical vector is indicated by the double-headed arrows. **A:** After 3 days in unpolarized white light. **B:** After 3 days in polarized white light. **C:** After 3 days in unpolarized light followed by 2 days in polarized light. Note the sharp change in direction of growth (indicated by the single-headed arrow) upon placing the plant in polarized light.

The response to light has been carefully studied in spores of *Equisetum*. In this plant the spores become maximally sensitive to light three to four hours after inoculation onto the medium. (Swelling of the spore is complete within a few minutes.) Haupt (1958) made careful studies of the light-sensitive phase and concluded that there are two light reactions in the germination of *Equisetum* spores, a low-energy reaction and a high-energy reaction. The high-energy reaction had an energy requirement 100 to 1,000 times higher than the first (low-energy) reaction. The second (high-energy) reaction resulted in a more effective orientation of the germination axis. Meyer zu Bentrup (1963) studied both reactions in fertilized eggs of the brown alga, *Fucus*, as well as in spores of *Equisetum*. He concluded that two different photoreceptor chromophores are involved in the light reactions in both plants: a carotenoid in the form of a chromoprotein participates in the low-energy reaction and riboflavin might be the pigment involved in the high-energy reaction. The photoreceptor molecules have not been studied in detail in ferns. On the other hand, Jaffe and Etzold (1965) concluded that the phytochrome molecule is involved in the orientation of polarity in *Funaria hygrometrica,* at least under low and medium light intensities.

The action of polarized light on the orientation of germination suggests an anisotropic, dichroic structure of the photoreceptor chromophore (Jaffe, 1958; Jaffe and Etzold, 1965). In the spores of *Osmunda* and *Equisetum* these photoreceptor molecules occur in the peripheral cytoplasm close to the cell wall and are periclinally oriented (i.e., their absorption axes are parallel to the cell wall). Under low light intensities the photoreceptor molecules in *Funaria* appear to lie at random in the cytoplasm with respect to the cell wall; at higher intensities these molecules become oriented periclinally (Jaffe and Etzold, 1965).

As in many areas of higher cryptogam biology, our current information suggests more problems than it has solved. Not only are there many gaps in our knowledge of the effects of light in orienting polarity during germination, but there is still much to be learned about the nature of the photoreceptor chromoproteins and about how absorption of light energy ultimately results in the orientation of polarity.

Moss Gametophore Initiation

The development of the leafy gametophore of moss as a lateral outgrowth from the protonema was described in Chapter 4. The influence of the environment on the timing of gametophore initiation has long been known. Early experiments by Klebs (1893) showed that a relatively high light intensity is needed for gametophore initiation, whereas a weaker illumination permits indefinite protonemal growth. Buds do not develop in the dark. The nonphotosynthetic role of light in bud initiation was shown by Mitra, Allsopp, and Wareing (1959), who found a specific red light requirement for bud initiation by using sugar-supplemented media. Excellent protonemal growth with normal caulonema development occurs under blue light, although buds do not develop (Figure 5·4A). Likewise, buds do not develop when protonema is grown under green or far-red light or in darkness. Because far-red light does not cancel the effect of red light in bud initiation, it was concluded that the reversible red–far-red pigment system does not operate in this developmental sequence. The biochemical differences between cells grown under red and blue light are still largely unexplored. Some workers have suggested that red light is needed for the synthesis of some substance involved in the initiation of bud development.

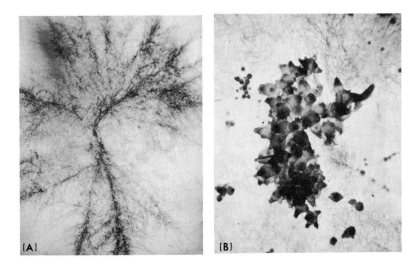

Figure 5·4. Effect of cytokinin on moss gametophore initiation in *Funaria hygrometrica*. A: Protonema grown in blue light. **B:** Protonema grown same length of time in blue light, but with kinetin (10^{-4} g/liter) added to the culture medium. Note the numerous gametophore buds.

A number of substances have been tested for their ability to initiate buds. Sugars such as sucrose and glucose, although they advance the timing of bud initiation, probably by speeding up growth in general, are unable to stimulate bud initiation in the dark. Similarly, auxins and gibberellins (Figure 5·5A,B), two classes of plant growth hormones (see Torrey, this series) at physiological concentrations have little effect on bud initiation in the light. They have no effect in the dark. However bud initiation is stimulated by the application of cytokinins, which are adenine derivatives and represent a third class of phytohormones (Figure 5·5C,D). Cytokinins induce bud formation under far-red, green, and blue light as well as red light (Figure 5·4B), and induction also occurs in dark-grown cultures (Szweykowska, 1963). The cytokinins are the only substances that obviate the red light requirement in the moss gametophore system.

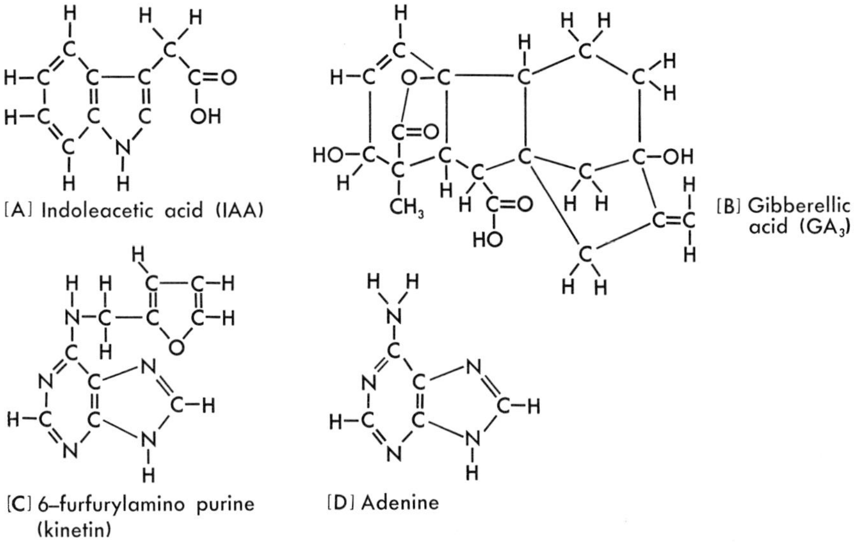

[A] Indoleacetic acid (IAA)

[B] Gibberellic acid (GA₃)

[C] 6–furfurylamino purine (kinetin)

[D] Adenine

Figure 5·5. Representatives of three classes of growth regulatory substances in plants.

Discovery of the cytokinin effect on bud initiation stimulated considerable research, which has been reviewed recently by Bopp (1968). Bud initiation offers a relatively simple system for the study of the mode of hormone action in that cytokinin activity is restricted to a specific morphogenetic effect and the filamentous protonema allows direct microscopic examination.

Brandes (1967) used fluorescence microscopy and acridine orange, a vital fluorochrome dye that combines with RNA, to study the timing of the early stages in bud induction. Although the first morphological sign of bud induction (the outgrowth of the filament that gives rise to the bud) occurs some sixteen to eighteen hours after hormone application, the first cytological sign of hormone effect occurs within ten hours. This is seen as the accumulation of fluorescent material, in this case represented by the acridine orange-RNA complex, in those cells that are capable of responding to the hormone, but not in nonresponding cells. Stimulation of soluble RNA (sRNA) synthesis is a well-known cytokinin effect in plants, but is probably a consequence, not a cause, of hormone-induced differentiation.

The accumulation of radioactive cytokinin in caulonema cells that are capable of giving rise to buds and in the buds themselves was shown by Brandes and Kende (1968). Conversely, nonreactive cells contain little radioactivity. They also found that when washed free of exogenously applied cytokinin during early bud formation, the developing buds (probuds) gave rise to protonemal filaments rather than to gametophores. The data suggest that the hormone must be present during some critical period of time until the switch to a new developmental pathway is stabilized. Cytokinin does not appear to act as a "trigger" in development. The data also suggest that the hormone which is easily removed by washing is the physiologically active form. A possible role for cytokinin at the level of translation, rather than transcription, is suggested by the rapid accumulation of the hormone in the cytoplasm of responsive cells.

The mode of action of the cytokinins, however, remains unknown, despite intensive research. Some experiments suggest an action through transfer RNA (tRNA) in gene controlled protein biosynthesis. This suggestion is based on the following kinds of evidence. Some, but not all, of the tRNA's of the soluble RNA fraction of cells have been found to have cytokinin activity. Specifically serine, isoleucine, and tyrosine tRNA's exhibit cytokinin activity, whereas arginine, glycine, phenylalanine, or valine tRNA's lack this activity. Other experiments have shown that radioactive benzylaminopurine, a cytokinin, is incorporated into certain tRNA's, but not into all of them. Moreover, serine tRNA (which has cytokinin activity) contains a cytokinin molecule as an integral part of the tRNA molecule. Even more interesting is that this cytokinin molecule is adjacent to the anticodon of serine tRNA and its presence is required for the attachment of serine tRNA to messenger RNA (mRNA). The strategic location of a cytokinin molecule adjacent to the anticodon of a specific tRNA molecule suggests the possible hormonal regulation of development by control of one or more steps in the translation of gene controlled protein synthesis. This view, however, has been contested by other investigators. For example, Kende and Tavares (1968) present evidence that the cytokinins are not precursors in the synthesis of sRNA and that the incorporation of cytokinin into sRNA is not related to the mode of action of the hormone. They suggest rather that cytokinins probably interact with their site of action by loose, probably noncovalent bonds. Thus cytokinins may exert their control over development by binding to specific sites in the cell. The nature of the binding site awaits further investigation.

In moss protonema exogenously applied cytokinins have their effect only on cells that are in the correct physiological state. The transient nature of the differentiated state becomes evident from the following type of experiment. When caulonema cells grown on a medium lacking cytokinin are transferred to fresh medium with cytokinin, buds develop as expected. On the other hand, when caulonema cells grown in the same way are transferred to fresh medium lacking cytokinin and are allowed to grow on this medium for a short period of time (from several to ten hours) before cytokinin is added, there is a dramatic decrease in the number of buds developed. The half-life of bud formation is on the order of five hours (Bopp and Diekmann, 1967). Differentiated caulonema cells placed on a cytokinin-less medium lose their ability to react; they have dedifferentiated. The unresponsive cells are non-reactive presumably because they have lost their binding sites for cytokinin.

Although there is no doubt about the effectiveness of exogenously supplied cytokinins in stimulating bud initiation, there is also evidence for the existence of endogenous regulators of bud development. A naturally occurring substance, called *factor H,* in protonema that stimulates bud initiation has been shown by Klein (1967). At low concentrations factor H exclusively promotes bud initiation. Another substance, called *bryokinin,* was isolated by Bauer (1966) from callus cultures derived from sporophytes of a moss hybrid (*Funaria hygrometrica* × *Physcomitrium piriforme*). Bryokinin is an adenine derivative and has cytokinin activity, including that of moss bud stimulation. These data indicate that cytokinins or related phytohormones are involved in the normal switching process in moss gametophyte development.

In summary, there is a light (specifically red light) requirement for bud initiation; only cytokinins replace this light requirement. Under natural conditions there presumably is a build-up of a phytohormone (factor H, bryokinin, or other) in the caulonema until a threshold concentration is reached. Only differentiated cells can react. In studies with exogenously supplied cytokinins, the hormone appears to act by combining with specific binding sites in the reactive cells. The physiologically active hormone is probably loosely bound by noncovalent bonds. Continued study of the moss gametophore initiation system is likely to provide additional data on the mechanism of hormone action in general. The cellular localization of hormone-specific binding sites would be an important advance in understanding the mode of action of hormones.

Development of the Fern Prothallus

In ferns, spore germination is followed by a period of filamentous growth. This growth phase is referred to as chloronemal or one-dimensional growth. The extent of filamentous growth is variable, depending on the species and the environment. Cell division during one-dimensional growth is strictly apical, with new cell walls formed perpendicular to the long axis of the filament. A change in the plane of cell division in the apical cell leads to the development of two-dimensional growth, and later to the development of the three-dimensional prothallus of the mature gametophyte.

Transition from one-dimensional to two-dimensional growth is a photomorphogenetic response. Darkness permits growth as the uniseriate filament only, and no substance has yet been found that obviates the need for light in normal gametophyte development. Both light quantity and light quality play an important role in the formation of the two-dimensional prothallus. In ferns (and in *Equisetum*) low light intensities and short photoperiods generally extend the filamentous growth phase, whereas higher light intensities and longer daily illumination accelerate the development of the two-dimensional plant.

Detailed studies on the light requirement by a number of investigators using a variety of ferns have shown a widespread if not universal need for blue light in normal fern development (Figure 5·6). In all cases blue light (of wavelengths less than 500 nm) of sufficient intensity

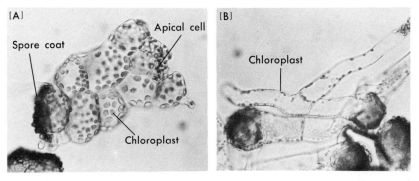

Figure 5·6. Effect of light on the development of the fern prothallus of *Polystichum minutum*. A: Early development of two-dimensional growth in blue light. **B:** Red light. Continued one-dimensional growth. Plants in **A** and **B** of same age and grown under equivalent energy levels. [Photos courtesy of Robert Fisher.]

stimulates two-dimensional growth. In wavelengths longer than 500 nm, including those of red light, the gametophytes usually remain filamentous. Only a single photochemical reaction appears to participate in the light-dependent response (Davis, 1968). The photoreceptor for blue light is probably a flavoprotein (or other yellow pigment). Yeoh and Raghavan (1966) have suggested riboflavin as the chromophore, but this needs verification.

The process of differentiation is usually considered to follow the synthesis of RNA and the formation of specific proteins, especially enzymes. Several experiments have dealt with this aspect of fern development. Normal development in white light is correlated with an increase in protein content per plant. Likewise, plants precultured in red light show a similar increase in protein when they are next placed in blue light. However, the rate of cell division also increases in blue light (relative to that in red light) and, when determined on a per cell basis, the protein content actually decreases. Plants grown in blue light have more cells than do those grown under equivalent energy levels of red light. Moreover, chloroplast volume is greater in blue light than in red light (compare chloroplast size in Figure 5·6A with that in Figure 5·6B). Bergfeld (1964) indicated that most of the increase in protein per plant in blue light is associated with chloroplast development. Increased RNA synthesis also occurs in blue light but most of this too is probably related to the synthesis of chloroplast proteins. The bulk of the increase in RNA and in protein can be interpreted as being a consequence, rather than the cause, of differentiation.

The preceding information on RNA metabolism does not necessarily exclude the possibility that a small fraction of the total RNA synthesized leads to the formation of small quantities of specific proteins needed for the transition from one- to two-dimensional growth. Drumm and Mohr (1967) measured the incorporation of ^{14}C-uridine into RNA and found that there was a distinct increase in RNA between three and six hours after plants previously cultured in red light were transferred into blue light. This early increase in RNA occurs just prior to or concurrent with the earliest observable morphological indications of morphogenesis, which are the widening of the apical cell in blue light and changes in the nuclear and nucleolar volume. The apical cells of red-grown plants contain large nuclei and nucleoli, whereas apical cells of plants grown in blue light have small nuclei and nucleoli (Bergfeld, 1967). When red-grown plants are placed in blue light, or vice versa, typical changes in nuclear and nucleolar volume become visible after three hours.

Further evidence for the involvement of RNA and protein in the change in form comes from studies with inhibitors. Two-dimensional growth is prevented by RNA inhibitors (analogs of the purine bases, adenine and guanine, and the pyrimidine bases, cytosine and uracil), amino acid analogs, inhibitors of protein synthesis (e.g., chloramphenicol and puromycin), and actinomycin D (which inhibits DNA-dependent RNA synthesis). The results of experiments with inhibitors have been used by some students of fern development to support the interpretation that the synthesis of specific proteins is essential for the transition from one- to two-dimensional growth.

A working model (modified from a diagram by Ohlenroth and Mohr, 1964) for the effect of blue light on fern development is shown in Figure 5·7. In red light certain genes are active (derepressed), whereas others are repressed. A photochemical reaction in the receptor pigment (a flavoprotein or other yellow substance), which is located in the cytoplasm, is initiated by blue light. Products of this reaction directly or indirectly act to derepress specific genes in the nucleus. Production of mRNA in the nucleus leads to the formation in the cytoplasm of specific proteins (enzymes) that are involved in the development of the two-dimensional growth phase. Other mRNA leads to the synthesis of chloroplast proteins. According to this model it is evident that almost anything that interferes with RNA synthesis or function, or with protein synthesis or function, will also interfere with the transition from filamentous to two-dimensional growth.

An alternative explanation for the change from one-dimensional to two-dimensional growth has been advanced by Sobota and Partanen (1966, 1967) and Miller (1968). They suggest that the change in

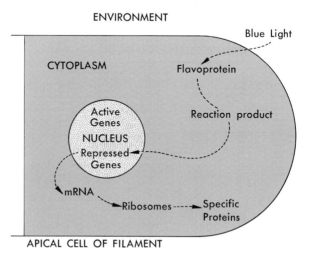

Figure 5·7. Diagrammatic model of the effect of blue light on fern morphogenesis. [Modified from a diagram by Ohlenroth and Mohr.]

form is related to the interaction between the rate of cell division and the rate of cell elongation. A high rate of cell division relative to the rate of cell elongation influences the plane of cell division and promotes the development of the two-dimensional gametophyte.

This idea stems from the early work of Errera (1883), who suggested that the geometry of the cell determines the plane of cell division. Although exceptions are known, this principle has widespread application in plant development. In his monumental treatise on Growth and Form, D'Arcy Thompson (1942) noted that in elongate meristematic cells severe restrictions on the plane of cell division permit divisions to occur only in a plane perpendicular to the long axis of the cell. Stebbins (1965, 1967) elaborated on this idea in order to explain the pattern of cell division in the meristematic cells of the grass leaf. He suggested that an interaction between the rate of cell division and the rate of cell elongation influences the plane of cell division in the grass leaf. A low rate of division permits the formation of elongate cells and, as indicated by Thompson, this tends to orient the mitotic spindle at right angles to the long axis of the cell. On the other hand, an increased rate of cell division would decrease the length of the cell at the time of the next division. As the cells become less elongate, the probability increases that the next division will occur in two planes in normally two-dimensional tissue (such as the two-dimensional fern gametophyte) or in three planes in normally three-dimensional tissue (such as the midrib tissue of the older fern prothallus).

If the rates of cell division and cell elongation play an important role in fern morphogenesis, then any agent that differentially affects cell division vis-à-vis elongation should also influence the transition from one- to two-dimensional growth. Most, if not all, of the experimental results with inhibitors can be interpreted to support this hypothesis.

Light differentially influences the rate of cell division and cell elongation. High light intensities induce more rapid cell divisions than does lower illumination and the two-dimensional plant develops earlier under higher illumination. Both cell division and the transition to two-dimensional growth are stimulated by blue light. Conversely, equivalent energy levels of red light sustain a lower rate of cell division and, with it, filamentous growth. Growth differences in red and blue light are maintained even when the energy levels are adjusted so that the rate of cell division under red and blue light is nearly the same. For example, after four days of growth in red light at 400 ergs/cm^2 per second and in blue light at 50 ergs/cm^2 per second, the cell numbers in the bracken fern *Pteridium aquilinum* were nearly the same (Sobota and Partanen, 1966). However, the individual cells of the plants grown under red light were more elongate than those in the blue. Red light promotes cell elongation and, with it, filamentous growth.

The results from most, if not all, of the studies on the effects of RNA and protein inhibitors and analogs of amino acids and nucleic acids can be interpreted to support the contention that differential cell division and elongation control the development of form (Miller, 1968). Rather than inhibiting the synthesis of specific proteins needed for development, these compounds appear to have a nonspecific effect on growth in general and thereby alter the relative rates of cell division and cell elongation. For example, Raghavan (1968) found that the progressive inhibition in the transition to two-dimensional gametophytes by high concentrations (50 to 100 mg/liter) of actinomycin D is correlated with a reduced rate of cell division. The number of cells in the one-dimensional plants eventually surpasses the cell number at which the two-dimensional growth in the untreated controls normally begins, indicating that growth is not completely inhibited by actinomycin D.

Indoleacetic acid (IAA), a naturally occurring plant growth hormone, also inhibits the transition to two-dimensional growth (Miller, 1968). One of the known functions of IAA is to stimulate cell elongation. Miller found that gametophytes of *Onoclea sensibilis* grown under white light remain filamentous in the presence of 10^{-7}M IAA even though these plants contained as many cells as the control plants when they were 90 per cent two-dimensional. Transition to two-dimensional growth was inhibited, but growth was not. IAA, like red light, increases the rate of cell elongation relative to cell division.

As indicated earlier, substances that slow the relative rate of cell division (e.g., actinomycin D) or speed the relative rate of cell elongation (IAA) inhibit the transition to two-dimensional growth. Substances that speed the rate of cell division relative to cell elongation should advance the time of transition to the two-dimensional gametophyte. One such compound, 2-chloroethyltrimethylammonium chloride (CCC), does just that. Kelley and Postlethwait (1962) showed that CCC at 10^{-4}M to 10^{-6}M promotes the transition from one- to two-dimensional growth in white light. CCC thus mimics blue light in the stimulation of cell division.

Fern gametophyte development is an area of active research and future work should clarify the significance of protein synthesis and differential cell division and cell elongation in fern development. Of special interest are the earliest changes that occur in the apical cell after filamentous plants are placed in blue light. The early widening and inhibition of elongation of the apical cell shows that a change in the architecture of the cell wall precedes cell division. Whether this change is correlated with a change in the orientation of cytoplasmic microtubules should be studied. The site of action of the product of the photoreaction also needs to be determined. The development of the fern gametophyte offers a simple system amenable to experimentation and the results promise to have broad botanical implications.

Sex Determination

Sex determination (as the term is used in this book) is the genotypic basis of sexuality, the genetic potential of the organism for maleness, or femaleness, or monoecism. The phenotypic expression of the genetic potential will be the subject of the next section.

The word *sex* commonly conveys the idea of separate male and female organisms. This is embodied in the widespread symbolic use in biology of the shield and spear of Mars (♂) to denote maleness and of the hand mirror of Venus (♀) for femaleness. The symbols are combined (☿) for monoecious organisms. In the higher cryptogams one must remember that sexuality is expressed in the haploid generation, not in the diploid generation as it is in most animals including man. The gametophytes of the higher cryptogams are haplodioecious or haplomonoecious. Although an increasing body of information is available on the cytological correlates of sexuality in haplodioecious plants, almost nothing is known about the biochemistry of sex determination. Some of the higher cryptogams seem to be excellent organisms for research along this line, but they have been little used to date.

Some of the early experiments with plants that supported the genetic basis of sex determination were carried out by Él. and Ém. Marchal in 1906–1907 on the mosses *Bryum* and *Mnium*. The Marchals showed that spores of these mosses consistently give rise to either male or female plants. Further, they found that fragments of male gametophores upon regeneration give rise to male plants only. Similarly, female plant fragments give rise to female plants only. They carried the series of experiments one step further. The seta and base of the sporophyte capsule were cut into pieces and the fragments were allowed to regenerate new plants. In this case the regenerants did not look like the sporophytic tissue from which they were derived, but instead like gametophytes. Moreover, the gametophytes obtained from regeneration of sporophytic tissue produce gametes; the gametes, however, are diploid, not haploid. Upon close examination of the diploid gametophytes, the Marchals found that most of the plants were monoecious, producing both male and female gametangia, although some of the plants formed more of one type of sex organ than of the other. In the type of dioecious system studied by the Marchals, the haploid spore and the haploid gametophyte have the genetic potential for either maleness or femaleness; the factors that determine maleness and femaleness are brought together at syngamy and are segregrated at meiosis. The diploid sporophyte and, therefore, the diploid gametophytes derived from regeneration of sporophytic tissue have the genetic potential for both maleness and femaleness. Fortunately, the Marchals worked with a simple system that gave rather clear-cut experimental results. More recently, a large number of deviations from the expected results have been obtained in other mosses and the student should refer to the review article by Näf (1962) for this information.

The type of sex determination described by the Marchals implies the existence of chromosomes that contain genetic determinants for femaleness or maleness. A chromosome that is known to control sex determination is called a *sex chromosome*. The first identification of sex chromosomes in plants was made by C. E. Allen in 1917, working with the liverwort *Sphaerocarpos donnellii* (Figure 5·8). In *S. donnellii* the four spores formed following meiosis remain united in a tetrad, a condition that makes it possible to follow the fate of each of the four cells from a single meiotic division. Two spores of a tetrad give rise to female plants; two give rise to male plants. Allen showed that a dimorphic chromosome pair was correlated with sex differences (Figure 5·9). The female plant always has a very large chromosome, the *X chromosome,* in addition to seven smaller chromosomes, called

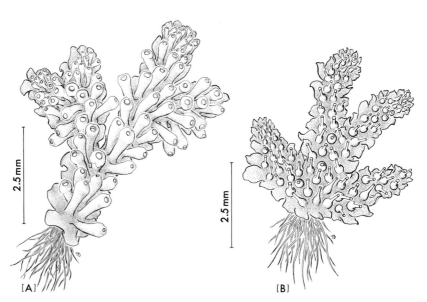

Figure 5·8. General morphology of the dioecious liverwort *Sphaerocarpos donnellii*. A: Female plant. **B:** Male plant.

Figure 5·9. Chromosome complements of
Sphaerocarpos donnellii. **A**: Female; note
the large X chromosome. **B**: Male, note the
very small Y chromosome.

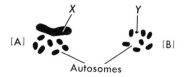

autosomes. The male plant has one very small chromosome, the *Y*
chromosome, in addition to seven autosomes. The dimorphic chromosomes are brought together at syngamy. During anaphase of Meiosis I
the dimorphic chromosomes move to opposite poles of the spindle.

The identification of dimorphic chromosomes correlated with sex
differences in *Sphaerocarpos donnellii* stimulated over thirty years of
productive cytologic and genetic research on this plant, notably by
Allen and his students in this country and by Knapp and his students
and Lorbeer in Europe. A few of their results will be given here (see
also the review articles by Allen, 1945, and Lewis, 1961). Sexuality in
S. donnellii, like that in the fruit fly, *Drosophila,* is dependent on an
X chromosome–autosome balance. Except for influencing sperm mo-
tility, the Y chromosome appears not to carry genes for maleness.
Evidence that the determinants for femaleness are carried on the X
chromosome comes from experiments by Knapp and Lorbeer. Lorbeer
used x-rays to induce mutations in female plants of *S. donnellii.* Upon
regeneration a few of the regenerants developed into male plants, rather
than female ones. Aberrations in the X chromosome were correlated
with sex transformation. Knapp, on the other hand, used x-rays on
sporophytes during meiosis. Subsequent tetrad analysis turned up an
occasional tetrad that gave rise to three, instead of two, male plants.
Cytological examination showed that the "extra" male plant contained a portion of the X chromosome in addition to the seven autosomes. From the experiments by Knapp and Lorbeer the conclusion
can be reached that sex transformation is due to an alteration in the
balance between the X chromosome and the autosomes. It is pertinent
to note here that male plants have never been known to give rise to
female plants.

One of the most conspicuous cytological features of sex chromosomes in plants and animals, and a feature that was recognized early
in the study of sex chromosomes, is the almost universal occurrence of
heterochromatin (Heitz, 1928). Heterochromatin is especially abundant in those chromosome segments that are concerned with the
sex-determining process. Sex chromosomes of some plants (e.g., the
X chromosome of *Sphaerocarpos drewii*) may be almost entirely
heterochromatic. Heterochromatin is so named because this portion of
the chromatin of the chromosome has a different coiling cycle than

does the rest of the chromatin, called *euchromatin*. Heterochromatin remains condensed and stains intensely during interphase, whereas euchromatin uncoils and therefore stains lightly. The two types of chromatin are chemically identical and are composed of the same four nucleic acids. Heterochromatic regions of the chromosomes do contain genes. However, because these regions remain condensed during interphase, the genes in the heterochromatic regions of the chromosome apparently exert physiological activity either rarely or at different times than do genes in the euchromatic regions. It is known that heterochromatic regions of the chromosome may replicate at different times than their euchromatic counterparts. The frequency of crossing over is also reduced in the vicinity of heterochromatin, and heterochromatin thereby may function to preserve the sex determinants as an hereditary unit during meiosis.

A large number of bryophytes are dioecious and many examples of an X-Y chromosome difference correlated with sex differences are known. The chromosomes are dimorphic in most cases, but in some the chromosomes differ cytologically only in the distribution of heterochromatin.

In dioecious organisms in which sexuality is determined by the segregation of factors at meiosis, the determinants for femaleness always appear to be grouped on a specific chromosome. The determinants for maleness, on the other hand, occur on autosomes and the Y chromosome. It seems unlikely that this type of dioeciousness could have evolved without the grouping of the genes for one of the sexes onto a specific chromosome, in this case the X chromosome.

A brief consideration of the adaptive advantages of dioeciousness versus monoeciousness will end this section. Dioeciousness is an enforced outbreeding system with the corresponding genetic advantages. However, the need for two separate plants to grow in close proximity in order for fertilization to occur can be a disadvantage during the colonization of new habitats by species with a dominant sporophytic generation. Perhaps it is significant that dioecious higher cryptogams are more common in the bryophytes where the gametophytic generation is dominant and characteristically has the capacity for vegetative reproduction. Gemmell (1950), in a study of the distribution of monoecious and dioecious moss species, found that dioecious species tend to be more widely distributed than monoecious ones. Dioecious species appear to be more adaptable, probably because of the genetic variation maintained in the interbreeding population as a result of obligate cross-fertilization.

The adaptive advantage of monoeciousness is that it would ensure the successful colonization of isolated territories by plants with a dominant diploid generation. Significantly, all the homosporous vascular cryptogams are monoecious. Monoeciousness increases the probability that fertilization will occur, which is of special significance during new habitat colonization. Functional monoecism occurs in some plants, such as *Sphaerocarpos,* in which the spores remain united in tetrads. United spore tetrads ensure that male and female sex structures develop in close proximity to each other. Furthermore, the male and female plants developing from spore tetrad germination are completely inter-fertile, at least in *Sphaerocarpos donnellii.*

Sex Expression

Sex expression is the phenotypic expression of the genetic potential of the organism. A few of the factors that influence the timing of sex expression have already been discussed; for example, in hornworts (see Chapter 4) and in *Selaginella* and *Isoetes* (see Homospory, Heterospory, and the Seed, Chapter 3). In this section sex expression in monoecious plants only will be discussed. The factors controlling the onset of antheridium and archegonium formation are different in these plants because intersexual structures are rare. However, in most cases very little is actually known about the physiology of induction of either type of gametangium.

The control of sex expression by a differential mitotic division occurs in a few higher cryptogams. The differential mitotic division results in the elimination of a chromosome or chromosomes from a cell lineage at a specific stage and place in the development of the plant. An early report of this type of division comes from studies by Haupt (1933) on the liverwort, *Marchantia grisea,* a species that grows in the Philippines and Sumatra. Two kinds of plants develop in this species: a unisexual male plant and a bisexual, although predominantly female, plant. The archegonia develop on the lower surface of the head of the archegoniophore, as is normal for species of *Marchantia* (see Figure 4·4B). Antheridia, however, may develop almost anywhere on the thallus of the bisexual plant, such as on the upper surface of the head of the archegoniophore. In some cases, whole thallus branches may be male. Detailed cytological studies by Haupt showed that the nuclei of the unisexual plant contain nine chromosomes, as do the nuclei in the male portions of the bisexual plant. The nuclei of the female portions of the bisexual plant, however, contain ten chromosomes. The additional chromosome is very small and heterochromatic, and was called a *z-chromosome* by Haupt. The presence of the z-chromosome, which is a sex chromosome, suppresses male tendencies and leads to the development of archegonia. Deletion of the z-chromosome during a differential mitotic division leads to the development of male sectors containing antheridia. Unisexual male plants may arise by regeneration from male sectors of the bisexual plants or from spores lacking the z-chromosome. In the latter case the z-chromosome may be eliminated during meiosis; spores with only nine chromosomes then give rise to unisexual male plants and spores with ten chromosomes give rise to bisexual plants. A spore tetrad may produce from one to four bisexual plants, depending on the timing of z-chromosome elimination during meiosis, if it is eliminated at all. At least one spore of the tetrad always gives rise to a bisexual plant. Unisexual female plants are unknown in *Marchantia grisea.*

Sex expression in the monoecious hornwort *Phaeoceros himalayensis* also is controlled by a differential mitotic division. In this species two small heterochromatic chromosomes, called *accessory chromosomes,* occur with five larger chromosomes in the nuclei of vegetative thalli and archegonia. The accessory chromosomes are eliminated from the cell lineage that gives rise to antheridia (Proskauer, 1967). Thus the presence of these small heterochromatic accessory chromosomes represses the expression of maleness in this hornwort.

There is no evidence that differential mitotic divisions influence sex expression in the majority of higher cryptogams. The conditions under which the gametophytes are cultured have a great influence on sex expression. For example, in crowded cultures of *Equisetum arvense* and *Equisetum telmateia* most spores will give rise to male gametophytes; a few spores will give rise to plants that bear archegonia only. However, the presence of the genetic potential for both maleness and femaleness is shown in cultures of single spores that characteristically give rise to gametophytes with both antheridia and archegonia (see Figure 4·28). It has not yet been established whether the difference in phenotypic expression in crowded cultures is due to nutritional deficiencies, hormonelike substances, the accumulation of waste products, or other factors.

Induction of antheridia in monoecious ferns is one of the most thoroughly studied examples of sex expression in the higher cryptogams. In ferns a period of antheridium formation usually precedes archegonium formation. Antheridium formation often begins when the gametophyte is young, prior to the development of the cordate prothallus. Archegonium formation begins after the development of the cordate prothallus and the base of the archegonium is embedded in midrib tissue. In some ferns the periods of archegonium and antheridium formation overlap in time; in others antheridium formation ceases prior to the onset of archegonium formation.

Döpp (1950) was the first to show that fern gametophytes produce a substance that influences the timing of sex expression in other gametophytes. He demonstrated that an extract of gametophytes of the bracken fern, *Pteridium aquilinum,* or the culture medium on which the bracken fern was growing, hastened the onset of antheridium formation in other gametophytes of this species and in prothalli of *Dryopteris filix-mas.* This substance, called an *antheridiogen,* hastens antheridium formation, but has no effect on archegonium formation. Other studies have shown that the antheridiogen from the bracken fern also hastens antheridium formation in many members of the family Polypodiaceae and in at least one member of the family Dicksoniaceae. However, the sensitivity to the bracken antheridiogen varies considerably in the species tested. This indicates that the antheridiogens of each fern species are chemically similar, but are not structurally identical. Complete chemical characterization and identification of the bracken fern antheridiogen is still to be done. The purified antheridiogen has the properties of a complex unsaturated carboxylic acid with a biologically active carboxyl group (Pringle, 1961). There is evidence that the molecule is active only in the free acid form. The molecule does not contain phosphorus or amino acids.

The *Pteridium* antheridiogen is inactive in members of the fern families Schizaeaceae, Osmundaceae, and Cyatheaceae. Subsequent investigations showed the occurrence of different antheridiogens in *Anemia phyllitidis* and *Lygodium japonicum* (members of the family Schizaeaceae). Although the antheridiogen from *A. phyllitidis* induces antheridia on *L. japonicum,* the antheridiogen of *L. japonicum* is inactive in *A. phyllitidis.* On the other hand, gibberellin (specifically GA_3) induces antheridium formation in both of the preceding species, but different concentrations are optimal. Näf (1968) has shown that the antheridiogens produced by *Pteridium, Anemia,* and *Lygodium* are different molecular entities, but their chemical identity is still unclear. The evidence indicates that the antheridiogens of *Anemia* and *Lygodium* might be structurally similar to the gibberellins, although they are different from any known gibberellins (Voeller, 1964). The existence of gibberellins within prothalli of *A. phyllitidis* has been demonstrated by Schraudolf (1966). The possibility that the gibberellins only mimic the effect of natural antheridiogens cannot yet be excluded.

Fern prothalli change in their sensitivity to antheridiogens during growth. In general, prothalli become sensitive to antheridiogens after a certain minimum cell number is exceeded. (This number varies with the species and the culture conditions, including the hormone concentration in the medium.) They generally lose their sensitivity soon after the cordate prothallus is formed.

Experiments with isolated prothalli have shown that an antheridiogen appears in the medium only after the gametophytes have lost their sensitivity to it. Antheridium formation ceases soon after the prothalli lose their sensitivity to antheridiogen. We have the interesting and biologically significant phenomenon of an organism beginning to form female reproductive structures at the same time that it is secreting into the medium substances that induce the expression of maleness in plants in its immediate vicinity. The occurrence of antheridiogens increases the opportunity both for fertilization and for outbreeding in a gametophytic population of monoecious ferns. More complete discussions of antheridiogens can be found in the reviews by Näf (1961), and Bopp (1968).

Embryo Development

The zygote, within the confines of the archegonium, begins development within several days after fertilization. In many plants four to six days elapse between fertilization and the first division of the zygote. In contrast to spores, an extended rest period does not occur. Polarity, a necessary prerequisite for differentiation, is already present in the fertilized egg of most, if not all, higher cryptogams. Polarity may be manifested by differences in the degree of vacuolization and in the distribution of cytoplasmic constituents between the two ends of the egg. The shape of the archegonium and the position of the archegonium on the gametophyte establish nutritional gradients across the egg. Moreover, the archegonium imposes physical restraint on the developing embryo. Division in the cells of the archegonium is one of the first events to be seen following fertilization, and the developing embryo becomes enclosed in a jacket consisting of at least two wall layers. The cells are turgid, but the amount of pressure exerted upon the developing embryo by the multilayered jacket has not been determined.

In most higher cryptogams the plane of the first division of the zygote is at right angles both to the polar axis of the zygote and to the long axis of the archegonium. In many ferns, in contrast, the plane of the first division is parallel to the long axis of the archegonium. The shoot apex of the embryo in the bryophytes, psilopsids, and sphenopsids develops toward the archegonium neck (Figure 4·29) and the opposite end of the embryo develops an absorbing region, called a foot, toward the base of the archegonium. In the two-celled embryos of lycopsids and some ferns, on the other hand, the cell toward the base of the archegonium gives rise to the main part of the embryo, and the cell toward the archegonium neck, called the *suspensor,* enlarges and serves to push the developing embryo into the gametophytic tissue. Consequently, the embryo grows into the gametophyte from which it derives its nutrition. The embryo ultimately grows out from the gametophyte.

Organogenesis during embryo development occurs with a remarkable degree of regularity in most higher cryptogams. In the vascular cryptogams this involves the organization of the shoot apex, the first leaf or leaves, and the root apex (except in the rootless psilopsids). Organ differentiation occurs prior to the rupture of the archegonium by the embryo. The time sequence of embryo development in the fern *Todea barbara* is given in Table 5·2.

TABLE 5·2
Time Sequence of Embryo Development of the Fern
Todea barbara

STAGE IN DEVELOPMENT	DAYS FOLLOWING FERTILIZATION
Unicellular	0–5
Foot initiation	15–16
Leaf initial present	18
Stem and root initiation	19–20
Differentiation of procambium	22
Emergence of embryo from the archegonium	30

SOURCE: From DeMaggio and Wetmore, 1961.

Although there is variation in detail, the general pattern of embryogeny in each class or subclass (as in the bryophytes) of higher cryptogams is remarkably uniform.

The zygote and the spore are two stages in the life cycle where the cell number is reduced to the minimum of one. The multicellular growth phases that normally develop from each of these cell types have dissimilar form and function. Whether the separate developmental pathways result from differences intrinsic to the cells themselves or from the different environments in which the spore and zygote develop has been for many years a matter for discussion. Within recent years experimental studies have yielded information on the influence of physical restraint by the archegonium wall, nutrition, and factors intrinsic to the zygote itself in the control of normal fern embryo development.

A discussion of the roles played by these factors in controlling the developmental pattern that leads to sporophyte organization will be followed by a discussion of factors that influence apogamous outgrowths of sporophytes from plants grown in culture.

The first experiments that attempted to analyze the influence of the archegonium on embryo development were carried out by Ward and Wetmore (1954) on the fern *Phlebodium aureum*. Because the zygote of this fern is firmly attached to the wall of the venter (and therefore it could not be removed), pressure on the developing embryo was relieved by surgically removing portions of the multicellular calyptra at the level of the gametophytic thallus. Otherwise the archegonium was left intact on the plant. The surgically treated embryos grow out from the archegonium usually as a cylindrical or somewhat irregular mass of cells. A regular pattern of cell division that leads to the early organization of the shoot apex, leaf, and root apex does not occur. Although much delayed, leaves, each with an associated shoot apex, ultimately develop on the thalloid "embryo" still attached to the gametophyte. These results may be interpreted as indicating that mechanical pressure from the archegonium determines the oriented division planes that lead to normal embryogeny in the intact archegonium; release of pressure by surgical treatment results in less regularity in the planes of cell wall formation. However, the ultimate formation of sporophytes indicates that sporophyte organization is not under the control of physical pressure of the archegonium, but under the control of factors either internal to the zygote and embryo or coming from the gametophyte.

Additional information comes from studies on the fern *Todea barbara* by DeMaggio and Wetmore (1961, and see also DeMaggio, 1963). The zygote of this fern is not attached to the archegonium wall, and, therefore, the unicellular and older embryos can be completely removed from the archegonium and their morphogenetic potentialities studied in culture. Unicellular embryos four to five days old were the youngest used in these studies (Figure 5·10A). Examination of cultured embryos isolated when four to five days old shows that the first few divisions occur in the same sequence as in the unexcised embryos. These divisions lead to the formation of the globular octant stage in fern embryogeny in both excised and unexcised embryos. However, the orientation of the mitotic spindle appears to be haphazard in post-octant stages of development of isolated embryos. The embryo gradually loses its globular appearance and develops into an irregular, flattish, frequently unbranched thalloid plant (Figure 5·10B). Some of the embryos even develop antheridialike, sterile structures, increasing the resemblance of the isolated embryo to a fern prothallus. The induction of leaf, stem, and root has not yet been accomplished in embryos isolated four to five days after fertilization. However, normal sporophyte development occurs when seventeen- and twenty-day-old embryos are isolated and cultured, as long as the proper nutritional environment

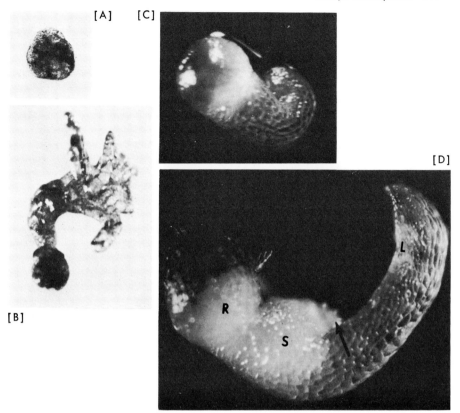

Figure 5·10. Embryo development of the fern, *Todea barbara*. A: Embryo isolated when still unicellular and cultured for one week. Note the globular shape.
B: Embryo isolated when still unicellular and cultured for four months. Note the
branched, thalloid outgrowth from the globular base. **C–D:** Embryos isolated 20
days after fertilization and cultured on a solidified medium containing sugar. **C:**
After 1 month in culture. **D:** Embryo after 4 months in culture. Primary leaf (L),
second leaf (arrow), stem region (S), and root region (R) are visible. [Photos courtesy of Dr. A. E. DeMaggio.]

is provided (Figure 5·10C,D). Seventeen-day-old embryos require
either autoclaved coconut milk (10 per cent) (which contains a variety
of growth factors) or inositol and sorbitol (25 mg/liter of each) in
addition to sucrose and mineral salts. Only the foot region is organized
in seventeen-day-old embryos (Table 5·2). Embryos isolated twenty
days after fertilization, after leaf, stem, and root initiation, require
only sucrose in addition to mineral salts.

The results may be interpreted as follows. Up to the globular octant
stage in development, embryogeny appears to be influenced more by
internal factors than by physical restraint from the archegonium or

nutritional factors from the archegonium and gametophyte. At the ultrastructural level the highly specialized nature of the egg of the fern, *Dryopteris filix-mas,* and the liverwort, *Sphaerocarpos donnellii,* has been described by Bell (1966) and Diers (1966), respectively. Biochemical differentiation accompanies morphological differentiation. One suggestion, based on analogy to sea urchin embryogenesis, is that long-lived "masked" mRNA occurs in the unfertilized egg. The masked mRNA would be activated upon fertilization and would determine the pattern of embryo development through the octant stage. (See the articles by Tyler, 1967, and Gross, 1967, for discussions of the role of long-lived mRNA in the determination of embryonic development in sea urchins.) According to this suggestion, the synthesis of new mRNA would then influence the development of postoctant stage embryos. However, note should be made that the existence of long-lived mRNA in the higher cryptogams has not been established. Moreover, the possibility that the mRNA under discussion is synthesized after fertilization during the four to five days before the first mitotic division has not been excluded.

The physical-chemical environment around the embryo is extremely important during postoctant embryo development. This environment determines whether normal sporophyte development will occur. If the requirements are not met, then a prothallial structure develops. Moreover, the nutritional requirements of embryos change during development with those of young embryos more complex than those of older ones. The physical-chemical environment that leads to normal sporophyte organization from embryos isolated four to five days after fertilization has not yet been determined. Thus the zygote normally gives rise to a plant with sporophytic organization primarily because of the physical-chemical environment maintained by the archegonium and gametophyte.

The influence of the environment on the determination of developmental patterns is shown even more dramatically by studies on the morphogenetic potentialities of young microspores of several species of tobacco (*Nicotiana* spp.) (Nitsch and Nitsch, 1969). In this study stamens isolated before the appearance of starch grains in the developing microspores were grown in vitro. Some of the microspores within the anthers gave rise to haploid plants with normal sporophyte form rather than to pollen grains. These haploid sporophytes developed normally and even produced flowers. Thus it appears that excision of stamens results in a changed environment at a critical time in microspore development and this permits a change in developmental pattern.

Physical pressure from the archegonium appears to have no direct effect on the developmental pathway leading to sporophyte organization. The multicellular wall of the archegonium appears to act primarily by restricting the direction and rate of enlargement of the cells of the embryo. This, in turn, affects the plane of cell division, as discussed in a previous section, the Development of the Fern Prothallus. Physical restraint has its greatest influence on embryo development between the octant stage and organ initiation. Once the organs have been initiated and metabolic gradients established within the embryo, physical restraint has less effect on influencing the timing of sporophyte development.

In ferns the sequence of development of the sporophyte from the zygote within the archegonium stands in marked contrast to the pattern of development of the sporophyte during apogamy. During apogamy the transition from gametophyte organization to sporophyte is a continuous process; the apogamous outgrowth slowly assumes the characteristics of the young sporophyte. There is no stage comparable to the zygote or embryo. The sporophyte generally arises from a thickened cushion in which develops an apical cell or a group of meristematic cells. There is no change in the ploidy level during the initiation or development of the sporophyte. Although they arise through quite different developmental sequences, the mature sporophytes produced sexually and apogamously do not differ in morphology.

The importance of nutrition in the induction of apogamous sporophytes of ferns in vitro has been shown by a number of workers (e.g., Whittier and Steeves, 1960, and Whittier, 1964). Apogamy in several ferns can be induced by manipulating the concentration of carbohydrates in the medium or by increasing the light intensity. An increase in the concentration of sugars (e.g., sucrose and glucose) leads to an increase in the number of apogamous sporophytes. For example, glucose at a concentration of 2.5 per cent induces the formation of apogamous outgrowths from gametophytes of *Pteridium aquilinum,* a fern that also forms sporophytes following sexual reproduction. Moreover, apogamous outgrowths from callus cultures of *Lycopodium* and of some mosses can be induced by the addition of appropriate concentrations of sugars and/or coconut milk.

The dramatic influence on developmental patterns of substances like simple sugars merits further comment. Exogenously supplied sugars (and increased light intensity) modify the carbohydrate nutrition of the plant possibly by increasing the respiratory substrates and by increasing the energy available for cellular function. Moreover, Bidwell, Barr, and Steward (1964) have shown in plant cultures that added sugar is preferentially utilized in protein synthesis. Exogenously supplied sugars lead to the formation of parenchymatous thickenings on the fern prothallus. It is possible that metabolic gradients established in the thickened tissue provide opportunity for differential activation of gene blocks or sequences, or the translation of mRNA already in the cytoplasm which leads to the organization of sporophyte form. In this view the carbohydrates should not be considered to have a direct regulatory function in controlling developmental pathways. Rather they aid in the establishment of an environment favorable for sporophyte development.

In contrast, Bauer (1956) and others have described the occurrence of a system in mosses in which increasing concentrations of sugar in the medium decreases the number of apogamous outgrowths. Here the presence of exogenously supplied sugar apparently forms an environment unfavorable for apogamous sporophyte development. The formation of apogamous outgrowths is, however, stimulated by chloral hydrate and increasing concentrations of nitrogen-containing compounds in the medium. In these mosses the apogamous outgrowths of the sporophytes arise directly from the protonema, in the same position as do the gametophore buds. Bauer has suggested that sporophyte organization is related to the persistence in the developing gametophore bud of an apical cell with two, rather than three, cutting faces. The sporophyte has an apical cell with two cutting faces, whereas the gametophore characteristically has an apical cell with three cutting faces. An apical cell with two cutting faces is first organized during development of the gametophore bud, but this is soon replaced by an apical cell with three cutting faces. How chloral hydrate and nitrogen modify conditions so that an apical cell with two cutting faces persists, if this is what occurs, awaits further study. Also to be determined is whether a truly haploid protonema can give rise to apogamous sporophytes. Polyploid series are common in mosses, and, unless chromosome numbers are checked, reports that apogamous outgrowths may arise from haploid plants may be erroneous. Unlike in ferns, functional spores are seldom produced by apogamous sporophytes in mosses and it is doubtful that apogamy in mosses would provide any selective advantage in nature.

In summary, a proper physical-chemical environment is necessary for the development of sporophyte organization in both apogamously and sexually reproducing plants. The effect of carbohydrates seems to be an indirect one. Added sugars help establish the correct environment which favors the activation of gene sequences that determine sporophyte form, or the translation of these messages. The more complex nutritional requirements of embryos probably are due to the highly specialized and heterotrophic nature of the zygote and the young embryo itself. During normal embryogeny the proper physical-chemical environment is maintained by the archegonium and gametophyte. In this view, the zygote gives rise to a sporophyte because of the environment in which the embryo develops. However, the first stages in embryogeny (up to the octant stage) appear to be under the control of factors within the embryo itself; whether these factors are already present in the unfertilized egg remains to be determined. It appears that the archegonium, especially in the vascular cryptogams, has its effect by bringing about the early differentiation of organ primordia. Presumably it does this by restricting the directions of cell enlargement and thereby influencing the planes of cell divisions. Thus the archegonium and the gametophyte together provide the correct environment for normal sporophyte development, and factors intrinsic to the zygote and physical pressure exerted by the archegonium together determine the particular pattern of embryo development within the archegonium. It should be clear from the foregoing that simply doubling the DNA (at fertilization) in itself does not determine sporophyte form.

Sporangium Development

A brief account of sporangium development leading to spore formation will close this chapter. This discussion will be limited to the results from experiments which concern the induction of the sporangium and the induction of meiosis in the spore mother cells. General comments on the sporangium and spore development occur in Chapter 2.

Other than in the ferns, few experimental studies have been undertaken to identify factors that regulate sporangium formation in the higher cryptogams. The sporangium represents the culmination of sporophyte development in plants like the bryophytes in which the sporangium is terminal on unbranched axes. Because of the continuous developmental sequence of the sporophyte of plants like bryophytes, the study of factors that specifically influence sporangium induction will be difficult. However, studies on sporangium induction might be carried out on plants like mosses which form capsules (containing the sporangium) in atypical locations. For example, diploid gametophores in some mosses occasionally form capsules apogamously at the tips of leaves of cultured plants that are aging and in which the medium is drying. (It is of interest that each leaf has an apical cell with two cutting faces, which is significant in connection with the previous discussion on the origin of apogamous outgrowths from moss protonemal buds.) The formation of sporangia on fronds of aging cultured plants of the fern *Todea barbara,* but not on actively growing plants, has been reported recently (DeMaggio, 1968). The mode of action of aging or staling of the medium on capsule and sporangium induction is unknown and the importance of these factors in sporangium induction in nature remains to be determined.

Fern leaf primordia have been useful tools for morphogenetic research, including the regulation of sporangium induction. Leaf primordia arise near the base of the apical cushion in ferns like the cinnamon fern (*Osmunda cinnamomea*). In the cinnamon fern an apical cell is initiated early in the development of the leaf primordium and it persists throughout the remainder of leaf growth (Steeves and Briggs, 1958). The shoot apex of this fern contains sets of leaves for four successive seasons; the outermost set expands each year and a new set is developed at the base of the apical cushion (Steeves and Wetmore, 1953). Thus the leaf of the cinnamon fern lives for four years, three within the bud and one in the mature, expanded form. Careful excision of the leaf primordia of the cinnamon fern followed by their

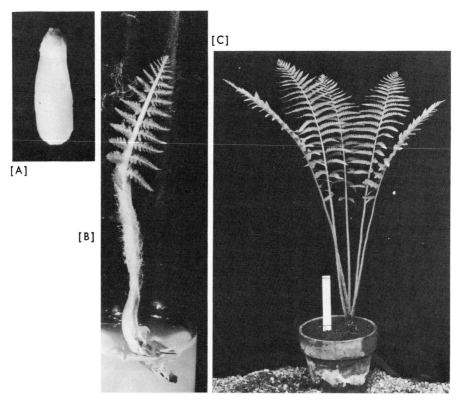

Figure 5·11. Fronds of the fern *Osmunda cinnamomea* grown *in vitro*. A: Leaf primordium at time of explantation to nutrient medium. B: Mature frond after explantation and culturing of primordium on basal medium. C: Plant with normal mature fronds for comparison. [Photos courtesy of Dr. T. A. Steeves.]

growth in organ culture has shown that the youngest primordia are not yet determined to be leaves. Instead they give rise to whole new plants. Somewhat older leaf primordia give rise to either whole plants or leaves. However, the tenth oldest primordium on the apical cushion and older ones all continue to grow as leaves when isolated and grown in culture. Organ culture of leaves of various ages has made possible the investigation of substances that influence sporangium induction in leaves that otherwise would remain sterile (Figure 5·11).

Sporangia can be induced on excised and cultured fern leaves when high concentrations (8 to 12 per cent) of sucrose are added to the culture medium (Sussex and Steeves, 1958). Calcium nitrate, in the presence of high sucrose concentrations, increases the number of fronds that develop sporangia and the number of sporangia on each frond. Sucrose probably plays an indirect role in the regulation of this developmental pathway, as was discussed in the previous section.

Although Sussex and Steeves (1958) were able to induce sporangium formation on isolated leaves, they found that the spore mother cells within these sporangia do not undergo meiosis. On the other hand, meiosis does occur when pinnae bearing sporangia already at the premeiotic spore mother cell stage of development are isolated and cultured (Clutter and Sussex, 1965). These results are intepreted as indicating that a specific substance, called a *meiotic stimulus,* must be present at the appropriate stage in sporangial development for meiosis to occur. Clutter and Sussex suggest that the meiotic stimulus comes from the shoot apex. This interpretation accounts for the failure of meiosis to occur in sporangia that develop on leaves isolated prior to sporangium formation, and the occurrence of meiosis in sporangia on pinnae detached from the plant after spore mother cell differentiation. Evidence for the existence of a meiotic stimulus also comes from studies in flowering plants on meiotic cells maintained in culture. However, the nature and mode of action of the meiotic stimulus is unknown.

Selected Bibliography

Alexopoulos, C. J., and H. C. Bold. *Algae and Fungi*. New York: Macmillan, 1967.

Allen, C. E. "The Genetics of Bryophytes II." *Botan. Rev.,* **11**:260–87, 1945.

Andrews, H. N. "Notes on Belgian Specimens of *Sporogonites*." *Palaeobotanist,* **7**:85–89, 1960.

Banks, H. P. "The Early History of Land Plants." Centennial Celebration of the Peabody Museum. Yale University, Symposium on the Evolution and Environment. New Haven, Conn., 1968.

Bauer, L. "Über Vegetative Sporogonbildung bei einer Diploiden Sippe von *Georgia pellucida*." *Planta,* **46**:604–618, 1956.

——— "Isolierung und Testung einer Kinetinartigen Substanz aus Kalluszellen von Laubmoossporophyten." *Z. Pflanzenphysiol.,* **54**:241–53, 1966.

———, and H. Mohr. "Der Nachweis des Reversiblen Hellrot-Dunkelrot-Reaktionssystems bei Laubmoosen." *Planta,* **54**:68–73, 1959.

Baxter, R. W., and G. A. Leisman. "A Pennsylvanian Calamitean Cone with *Elaterites triferans* Spores." *Am. J. Botany,* **54**:748–54, 1967.

Bergfeld, R. "Kern- und Nucleolusausbildung in den Gametophytenzellen von *Dryopteris filix-mas* (L.) Schott. bei Umsteuerung der Morphogenese." *Z. Naturforsch.,* **22b**:972–76, 1967.

Bidwell, R. G. S., R. A. Barr, and F. C. Steward. "Protein Synthesis and Turn-over in Cultured Plant Tissue: Sources of Carbon for Synthesis and the Fate of the Protein Breakdown Products." *Nature,* **203**:367–73, 1964.

Bold, H. C. *Morphology of Plants,* 2d. ed. New York: Harper & Row, 1967.

Bopp, M. "Control of Differentiation in Fern-Allies and Bryophytes." *Ann. Rev. Plant Physiol.*, **19**:361–80, 1968.

———, and W. Diekmann. "Versuche zur Analyse von Wachstum und Differenzierung der Moosprotonemen. V." *Planta*, **74**:86–96, 1967.

Boureau, É. *Traité de Paléobotanique. Tome II. Bryophyta, Psilophyta, Lycophyta.* Paris: Masson et Cie ,1967.

Bower, F. O. *The Origin of a Land Flora.* London: Macmillan, 1908.

Brandes, H. "Fluorescenzmikroskopische Analyse der Knospenanlagen von Moosprotonemen nach Anfärbung mit Acridinorange." *Planta*, **74**:45–54, 1967.

———, and H. Kende. "Studies on Cytokinin-controlled Bud Formation in Moss Protonemata." *Plant Physiol.*, **43**:827–37, 1968.

Brokaw, C. J. "Chemotaxis of Bracken spermatozoids." *J. Exp. Biol.*, **35**:192–212, 1958.

Bünning, E. *Entwicklungs- und Bewegungsphysiologie der Pflanzen.* Berlin: Springer-Verlag, 1953.

———, and H. Etzold. "Über die Wirkung von Polarisiertem Licht auf Keimende Sporen von Pilzen, Moosen und Farnen." *Ber. Deut. botan. Ges.*, **71**:304–306, 1958.

Clutter, M. E., and I. M. Sussex. "Meiosis and Sporogenesis in Excised Fern Leaves Grown in Sterile Culture." *Botan. Gaz.*, **126**:72–78, 1965.

Davis, B. D. "The Transition from Filamentous to Two-Dimensional Growth in Fern Gametophytes. I." *Am. J. Botany*, **55**:532–40, 1968.

Delevoryas, T. *Morphology and Evolution of Fossil Plants.* New York: Holt, Rinehart and Winston, 1963.

DeMaggio, A. E. "Morphogenetic Factors Influencing the Development of Fern Embryos." *J. Linn. Soc. (Botany)*, **58**:361–76, 1963.

———. "Meiosis *in vitro:* Sporogenesis in Cultured Fern Plants." *Am. J. Botany*, **55**:915–22, 1968.

———, and R. H. Wetmore. "Morphogenetic Studies on the Fern *Todea barbara.* III. Experimental Embryology." *Am. J. Botany*, **48**:551–65, 1961.

Diers, L. "On the Plastids, Mitochondria and Other Cell Constituents During Oögenesis of a Plant." *J. Cell Biol.*, **28**:527–43, 1966.

Döpp, W. "Eine die Antheridienbildung bei Farnen Fördernde Substanz in den Prothallian von *Pteridium aquilinum* (L.) Kuhn." *Ber. Deut. botan. Ges.*, **63**:139–47, 1950.

Doyle, W. T. *Nonvascular Plants: Form and Function.* Belmont, Calif.: Wadsworth, 1964.

Drumm, H., and H. Mohr. "Die Regulation der RNS-Synthese in Farngametophyten durch Licht." *Planta*, **72**:232–46, 1967.

Foster, A. S., and E. M. Gifford. *Comparative Morphology of Vascular Plants.* San Francisco: W. H. Freeman, 1957.

Freeberg, J. A. "The Apogamous Development of Sporelings of *Lycopodium cernuum* L., *L. complanatum* var. *flabelliforme* Fernald and *L. selago* L. *in vitro.*" *Phytomorphology,* **7**:217–29, 1957.

———, and R. H. Wetmore. "Gametophytes of *Lycopodium* as Grown *in vitro.*" *Phytomorphology,* **7**:204–217, 1957.

Gantt, E., and H. J. Arnott. "Spore Germination and Development of the Young Gametophyte of the Ostrich Fern (*Matteuccia struthiopteris*)." *Am. J. Botany,* **52**:82–94, 1965.

Gross, P. R. "The Control of Protein Synthesis in Embryonic Development and Differentiation." In *Current Topics in Developmental Biology,* Vol. 2. New York: Academic Press, 1967, pp. 1–46.

Harris, T. M. *The British Rhaetic Flora.* British Museum of Natural History, 1939.

Hauke, R. L. "A Taxonomic Monograph of the Genus *Equisetum* subgenus Hippochaete." *Beih. Nova Hedwigia,* **8**:1–123, 1963.

Haupt, G. "Beiträge zur Zytologie der Gattung *Marchantia* (L.). II." *Zeitschr. ind. Abstammungs- u. Vererbungslehre,* **63**:390–419, 1933.

Haupt, W. "Über den Primärvorgang bei der Polarisierenden Wirkung des Lichtes auf Keimende *Equisetum*-Sporen." *Planta,* **51**:74–83, 1958.

Hébant, C. "Signification et évolution des Tissus Conducteurs chez les Bryophytes." *Nat. Monspeliensia (Botany),* **16**:79–86, 1964.

———. "Structure et différenciation des Tissus Conducteurs dans le Gamétophyte des *Polytrichum.*" *Nat. Monspeliensia (Botany),* **18**:293–97, 1967.

Hendricks, S. B., and H. A. Borthwick. "Photoresponsive Growth." In *Aspects of Synthesis and Order in Growth,* 13th Growth Symposium. Princeton, N.J.: Princeton Univ. Press, 1954, pp. 149–69.

Heslop-Harrison, J. "Pollen Wall Development." *Science,* **161**:230–237, 1968.

Hoffman, G. R. "The Effects of Certain Sugars on Spore Germination in *Funaria hygrometrica* Hedw." *Bryologist,* **67**:321–29, 1964.

Horner, H. T., N. R. Lersten, and C. C. Bowen. "Spore Development in the Liverwort *Riccardia pinguis.*" *Am. J. Botany,* **53**:1048–1064, 1966.

Ingold, C. T. *"Spore Liberation."* Oxford: Clarendon Press, 1965.

Jaffe, L. "The Effect of Polarized Light on the Growth of a Transparent Cell." *J. Gen. Physiol.,* **43**:897–911, 1960.

———, and H. Etzold. "Tropic Responses of *Funaria* Spores to Red Light." *Biophys. J.,* **5**:715–42, 1965.

Kelley, A. G., and S. N. Postlethwait. "Effect of 2-chloroethyltrimethyl-ammonium Chloride on Fern Gametophytes." *Am. J. Botany,* **49**:778–86, 1962.

Kende, H., and J. E. Tavares. "On the Significance of Cytokinin Incorporation into RNA." *Plant Physiol.,* **43**:1244–48, 1968.

Klein, B. "Versuche zur Analyse der Protonemaentwicklung der Laubmoose. IV." *Planta,* **73**:12–27, 1967.

Klekowski, E. J., and H. G. Baker. "Evolutionary Significance of Polyploidy in the Pteridophyta." *Science,* **153**:305–307, 1966.

Lewis, K. R. "The Genetics of Bryophytes." *Trans. Brit. Bryol. Soc.,* **4**:111–30, 1961.

Machlis, L., and E. Rawitscher-Kunkel. "Mechanisms of Gametic Approach in Plants." In *Fertilization,* Vol. 1. New York: Academic Press, 1967, pp. 117–61.

Meyer zu Bentrup, F. "Vergleichende Untersuchungen zur Polaritätinduktion Durch das Licht an der *Equisetum*-Spore und der *Fucus*-Zygote." *Planta,* **59**:472–91, 1963.

Miller, J. H. "An Evaluation of Specific and Non-specific Inhibition of 2-Dimensional Growth in Fern Gametophytes." *Physiol. Plant.,* **21**:699–710, 1968.

Mitra, G. C., A. Allsopp, and P. F. Wareing. "I. The Effects of Light of Various Qualities on the Development of the Protonema and Bud Formation in *Pohlia nutans* (Hedw.) Lindb." *Phytomorphology,* **9**:47–55, 1959.

Mohr, H. "The Influence of Visible Radiation on the Germination of Archegoniate Spores and the Growth of Fern Protonema." *J. Linn. Soc. (Botany),* **58**:287–96, 1963.

Näf, U. "Developmental Physiology of Lower Archegoniates." *Ann. Rev. Plant Physiol.,* **13**:507–32, 1962.

———. "On Separation and Identity of Fern Antheridiogens." *Plant and Cell Physiol.,* **9**:27–33, 1968.

Nakazawa, S. "Morphogenesis of the Fern Protonema. III." *Phyton,* **14**:37–41, 1960.

Nitsch, J. P., and C. Nitsch. "Haploid Plants from Pollen Grains." *Science,* **163**:85–87, 1969.

Ohlenroth, K., and H. Mohr. "Die Steuerung der Proteinsynthese durch Blaulicht und Hellrot in den Vorkeimen von *Dryopteris filix-mas* (L.) Schott." *Planta,* **62**:160–70, 1964.

Paschke, M. "Sporenkeimung und Protonemaregeneration aus Blattzellen bei 55 Jahre Alten Pflänzchen von *Physcomitrium piriforme* (L.) Brid." *Naturwissenschaften,* **52**:16, 1965.

Paton, J. A., and J. V. Pearce. "The Occurrence, Structure and Function of the Stomata in British Bryophytes." *Trans. Brit. Bryol. Soc.,* **3**:228–59, 1957.

Pringle, R. B. "Chemical Nature of Antheridiogen-A, a Specific Inducer of the Male Sex Organ in Certain Fern Species." *Science,* **133**:284, 1961.

Proskauer, J. "Studies on Anthocerotales. VI:12. On Spiral Thickening in the Columella and its Bearing on Phylogeny." *Phytomorphology,* **10:**1–19, 1960.

———. "Studies on Anthocerotales. **VII:**13. On Day Length and the Western Himalayan Hornwort Flora, and on Some Problems in Cytology." *Phytomorphology,* **17:**61–70, 1967.

Raghavan, V. "Actinomycin D-induced Changes in Growth and Ribonucleic Acid Metabolism in the Gametophyte of Bracken Fern." *Am. J. Botany,* **55:**767–72, 1968.

Ridgway, J. E. "Factors Initiating Antheridial Formation in Six Anthocerotales." *Bryologist,* **70:**203–205, 1967.

Schopf, J. M. *et al.* "Erect Plants in the Early Silurian of Maine." *U.S. Geol. Survey,* Prof. Paper 550-D: D69–D75, 1966.

Schraudolf, H. "Nachweis von Gibberellin in Gametophyten von *Anemia phyllitidis.*" *Naturwissenschaften,* **53:**412, 1966.

Siegel, S. M. *The Plant Cell Wall.* New York: Pergamon Press, 1962.

———. "Evidence for the Presence of Lignin in Moss Gametophytes." *Am. J. Botany,* **56:**175–79, 1969.

Smith, J. L. "The Liverworts *Pallavicinia* and *Symphyogyna* and Their Conducting System." *Univ. Calif. Publ., Botany,* **39:**1–83, 1966.

Sobota, A. E., and C. R. Partanen. "The Growth and Division of Cells in Relation to Morphogenesis in Fern Gametophytes. II. The Effect of Biochemical Agents on the Growth and Development of *Pteridium aquilinum.*" *Canad. J. Botany,* **45:**595–603, 1967.

Stange, L. "Regeneration in Lower Plants." In *Advances in Morphogenesis,* Vol. IV. New York: Academic Press, 1964, pp. 111–53.

Stebbins, G. L. "Chromosomal Variation and Evolution." *Science,* **152:** 1463–1469, 1966.

———. "Gene Action, Mitotic Frequency, and Morphogenesis in Higher Plants." In *Control Mechanisms in Developmental Processes.* New York: Academic Press, 1967, pp. 113–35.

Steeves, T. A. "On the Determination of Leaf Primordia in Ferns." In *Trends in Morphogenesis.* New York: John Wiley & Sons, 1966, pp. 200–19.

———, and W. R. Briggs. "Morphogenetic Studies on *Osmunda cinnamomea* L.—The Origin and Early Development of Vegetative Fronds." *Phytomorphology,* **8:**60–72, 1958.

———, and R. H. Wetmore. "Morphogenetic Studies on *Osmunda cinnamomea* L.: Some Aspects of the General Morphology." *Phytomorphology,* **3:**339–54, 1953.

Sussex, I. M. "The Origin and Development of Heterospory in Vascular Plants." In *Trends in Plant Morphogenesis.* New York: John Wiley & Sons, 1966, pp. 140–52.

Sussman, A. S. "Physiology of Dormancy and Germination in the Propagules of Cryptogamic Plants." In *Handb. der Pflanzenphysiologie,* Bd. XV. Berlin: Springer-Verlag, 1965, pp. 933–1026.

Thompson, D'Arcy W. *Growth and Form,* Vol. 2. London: Cambridge Univ. Press, 1942.

Torrey, J. G. *Development in Flowering Plants.* New York: Macmillan, 1967.

Tyler, A. "Masked Messenger RNA and Cytoplasmic DNA in Relation to Protein Synthesis and Processes of Fertilization and Determination in Embryonic Development." In *Control Mechanisms in Developmental Processes,* Developmental Biol. Suppl., **1:**170–226, 1967.

Valanne, N. "The Germination Phases of Moss Spores and Their Control by Light." *Ann. Botan. Fennici,* **3:**1–60, 1966.

Voeller, B. R. "Antheridiogens in Ferns." In *Régulateurs Naturels de la Croissance Végétale,* Paris: Gif s/Yvette, 1964, pp. 665–84.

Ward, M., and R. H. Wetmore. "Experimental Control of Development in the Embryo of the Fern, *Phlebodium aureum* J. Sm." *Am. J. Botany,* **41:**428–34, 1954.

Whittier, D. P. "The Influence of Cultural Conditions on the Induction of Apogamy in *Pteridium* Gametophytes." *Am. J. Botany,* **51:**730–36, 1964.

————, and T. A. Steeves. "The Induction of Apogamy in the Bracken Fern." *Canad. J. Botany,* **38:**925–30, 1960.

Yeoh, O. C., and V. Raghavan. "Riboflavin as Photoreceptor in the Induction of Two-Dimensional Growth in Fern Gametophytes." *Plant Physiol.,* **41:**1739–42, 1966.

Zimmermann, W. "The Main Results of the 'Telome Theory.'" *Palaeobotanist,* **1:**456–70, 1952.

Index